THE ENDPAPER

ILLUSTRATED SCIENCE BOOKS

ASTRONOMY

ASTRONOMY

Written by H. C. King

Pictures by Terry Maloney

watts

*illustrated
science books*

FRANKLIN WATTS, INC.

575 LEXINGTON AVENUE

NEW YORK 22, N.Y.

ASTRONOMY

This book was designed and produced by Rainbird,
McLean Ltd, 11 Charlotte Street, London, W.1. It
was printed by L. van Leer and Co., N.V., Amster-
dam, Holland, and bound by Van Rijmenam N.V.,
The Hague, Holland. The paper was supplied by
Corvey, N.V., Amsterdam.

FIRST PRINTING 1960

Library of Congress Catalog Number 60–10811

Contents

ACKNOWLEDGMENTS
We are indebted to the following observatories for the photographs reproduced
on page 47, Yerkes; 90, Lick; 209, 211,
212, 221, 230 and 231 Mount Wilson and
Palomar; 210, Victoria, B.C.

About the author and artist

Henry Charles King PH.D., M.SC.,F.R.A.S., F.B.O.A.

Henry C. King, Chief Astronomer of the London Planetarium and President of the British Astronomical Association, developed an early interest in astronomy, fired off by being given Sir Robert Ball's *The Story of the Heavens* for his thirteenth birthday. He started making telescopes while still at school, and his enthusiasm for astronomy was strengthened by his being given the freedom of the astronomer Sir William Herschel's extensive library at Slough. After studying astronomy and mathematics at London University he went on to do his M.Sc. and Ph.D. in the history and philosophy of science. Following this he was for seven years senior lecturer in ophthalmic optics at Northampton College of Advanced Technology in London. Dr King has lectured widely and published numerous papers, articles and books on optics, the history of science and on planetaria, about which he has become the leading British authority. He collects astronomical books, enjoys playing the piano and gardening and is a Jaguar car enthusiast – going to most Goodwood race meetings. He is married and has two children.

Terry Maloney F.R.A.S.

Mr Maloney, free-lance artist and writer, is a member of the British Astronomical Association and has done writing and illustrations for a number of scientific and astronomical works. He has, too, written and illustrated several books on astronomy, besides one on the construction of telescopes and instruments for astronomy. Mr Maloney has also had wide experience in other fields: he was in charge of a technical advice department in a firm of scientific instrument suppliers and has worked in advertising both in the art side and preparing copy.

The publishers are grateful to Dr Fletcher Watson, Professor at Harvard University, School of Education; Instructor in Astronomy, Harvard University, 1936–38, Research Associate, Harvard Observatory 1938–41, for his help in the preparation of this book.

About this book

The time has long passed since one could tell the story of astronomy with completeness in a single book. So rapid and varied have been the developments in this science, particularly during the last fifty years, that entire volumes can now be devoted to any one of its individual aspects. Even so, the vast majority of readers anxious to know something about the realm of the stars will turn first to a book on general astronomy. The information found in it will, of course, have been selected and sifted by its author, whose task is to present an overall picture in a lucid and attractive way.

In this book the reader is not only given a broad view of astronomy but also taken in easy stages from simple to more difficult concepts. It is, for example, a matter of common experience that the sun travels across the sky in a general east-to-west direction, that the moon undergoes a change in shape and position during a lunar month, and that the stars move overhead during the hours of night. These and similar basic observations are mentioned at the outset, but in a historical setting. Astronomy rests on the sure foundations of systematic observation carried out over long periods of time; in early times this observation had to be by the naked eye alone, and it was also largely spasmodic. Difficulties arise, however, when the observations are not interpreted correctly. It was once thought, for example, that the sun and stars actually traveled round the earth and that the moon actually changed its shape. The nature of the changes in these and similar viewpoints is one of the main themes of this book. Every opportunity is taken to remind the reader that the earth is a globe spinning in space, that as a planet it is just one of nine planets which move round the sun; that the sun is a moving star, and as such is a member of the great Milky Way galaxy or star city; that the Milky Way is just one galaxy in a realm of galaxies which constitutes the present observable material universe.

This is a book for the reader whose interest in objects in the heavens usually varies inversely with the distances of those objects. Information about parochial matters—about the sun, moon and planets—therefore occupies well over a third of the text. The space allotted to the stars is nevertheless adequate, bearing in mind the fact that the material is intended to serve as an introduction to what is now a vast subject. There is also an early chapter on the methods of observation and a final one which tells of developments in space flight. The use of mathematics has been purposely avoided, the one aim being to simplify the discussion as far as possible without sacrificing essential truth. A knowledge of mathematics and science will naturally help, but since many may not be familiar with the terminology of astronomy in particular and science in general, a glossary of terms is included.

Great care has been taken to differentiate between observations and inferences from observations. It is not true to say, for example, that astronomers observe dust-storms on the planet Mars. Rather are the surface markings of that planet temporarily obscured by yellowish patches, considered by most astronomers to be the effect of dust-storms. Nor is it true to say that the universe is expanding, thereby implying that this is either an established fact or something directly observable. Instead, astronomers measure red-shifts in the lines of the spectra of galaxies and generally interpret these shifts as a Doppler-Fizeau effect. Observation must always go hand-in-glove with theory, but in this book every attempt has been made to indicate which is observation and which is theory. By doing this the reader is not only given some slight insight into the methods of science but is also encouraged to realise that the advance of astronomy is a tentative and probing process—that astronomers estimate rather than measure the distances of the stars; that they look at optical images of the planets rather than at the planets themselves; that they think in terms of probability—if the facts do not fit the theory then the theory is the thing to alter, not the facts.

NOTE: Entries in SMALL CAPITALS indicate
that they appear in the glossary

1. Before the telescope

Astronomy, probably the most ancient of the sciences, has origins forever lost in the mist of prehistory. Many of its rich and varied traditions can be traced back some three to four thousand years, and from the earliest extant historical records can be inferred the beliefs and notions of a much earlier period.

In all probability the ever-changing aspect of the night sky was watched with interest by the first agriculturists – by settlers on the fertile plains of southern Mesopotamia, by the banks of the Indus, or on the Nile delta. For these and other peoples the regular appearances of the sun, moon, and stars stood out in marked contrast to the vicissitudes of life below. The gods might decree years of fatness, but crops were blighted, food went rotten, cattle grew sick, and men sometimes fell like corn-stalks before the reaper. Yet in the skies above the sun pursued an unwearied way, ever victorious over the powers of darkness, and through the cycle of the seasons set the imprint of law and order on apparent chaos. The moon waxed and waned unfailingly, the patterns of the stars seemed fixed for all eternity.

Because the sun dominated the heavens, ordered time, and conditioned the activities of men, it came to be regarded as one of the greatest, if not the greatest, of the gods. As a brilliant divinity he daily traversed the sky and at the blaze of noon caused men to seek cooling water and the protective shade. He was a deity to be reckoned with – to be placated through worship and thank-offer-ings. In the cloudless skies of Egypt he was supreme among the gods, reigning in heaven as his counterpart, the divine pharaoh, reigned on earth. From his sacred bark he poured out gifts of life and light. Having arrived at the western horizon in an exhausted condition, or as was sometimes thought, as an old man, he had to be lighted through the Egyptian underworld and then resurrected for yet another circuit of the sky. In Babylonia the sun god Sha-mash, later identified with Marduk, Ashur and other deities, is said to have drawn up codes of laws and counseled kings on all matters of state. Sometimes he was portrayed as an old man with flowing beard carrying a staff, sometimes he was shown seated in a chariot drawn by mules.

The kindlier moon was also regarded as an important deity. Its silvery radiance restricted the activities of demons and removed most of the terrors of darkness. It was a blessing to the traveler and nomad as he crossed the desert wastes in the cool of the night. The god Shamash was the son of the Babylonian moon god, Sin, and head of the old Sumerian pantheon. Seldom in early times was the moon given precedence over the sun in this way. In ancient Egypt the god of wisdom, Thoth, had lunar associations, but he came well below the sun god Ra in importance, while Chons, the moon god, was a quite insignificant deity. No doubt the Sumerians were impressed by the way the moon's phases appeared to reflect within a month the patterns of growth of plants and animals. Un-aware that the moon is a dark body which shines only because it reflects sunlight, they regarded it as a deity capable of monthly resurrection. Yet in time Sin's prestige waned in favor of that of the sun god Marduk, and the attribute of fertility passed to Ishtar, goddess of the PLANET Venus. Significantly enough, the role of the moon as a universal procreator is found in many early religions; the mother-goddesses Astarte, Ashtoreth, Isis, Artemis, Hera and Diana all had lunar attributes.

According to the writer of the first chapter of the Book of Genesis, the lights in the sky were put there to divide the day from the night, to act as signs of the progress of days, seasons and years, and to illumine the earth for the benefit of mankind. The priests

According to the ancient Egyptians, night presented day
every morning with a new-born sun.

of Sumeria, Babylonia and Egypt, while not sharing in the Hebraic
monotheism, likewise used these aspects of divine providence.
They noticed the diurnal motion of the stars – how stars which
appeared above the eastern horizon moved as a whole across the
sky, and set below the western horizon. Many stars, however,

neither rose nor set, being always above the horizon, but even these, in common with the rest, appeared to move around one fixed point. This point we now call the NORTH CELESTIAL POLE. A star at this point would have no apparent motion during the course of a night. This is because it marks the place where the earth's axis of rotation, if continued in a long line through the north pole, would meet the northern aspect of the starry sky.

The apparent diurnal motion of the stars is due, of course, to our position on the rotating earth. The ancients knew nothing of this, nor of the fact that the earth is a globe some 8000 miles in diameter. Instead, they were content to regard it as flat and bounded by mountains or the limits of the sea. Some Egyptian drawings even show the stars hanging like so many lamps from the flat ceiling of the sky which presumably was given a solidity similar to that of the earth.

The priests also noticed the different seasonal aspects of the night sky. To assist in keeping track of these appearances and to make star identification easier, they arranged the stars into various arbitrarily-chosen groups or CONSTELLATIONS bearing the figures of men and animals. Through continued observation they came to know that when certain prominent star groups like the Pleiades or bright stars like Sirius would be seen near the sun at sunrise or at sunset. It became evident that in the course of a year the sun appears to make a complete circuit of the starry heavens, moving slowly eastwards against the background of the stars at a rate requiring about 360 days for a complete trip around the sky. This annual motion of the sun is brought about by the earth's annual revolution around the sun, but this was completely unknown in ancient times.

Connected with the progress of the sun in its annual cycle were the seasonal changes in its midday height as indicated by the varying lengths of shadows cast at noon. Also changing throughout

The 12 "long" hours of daylight and 12 "short" hours
of night at the summer solstice.

The 12 "short" hours of daylight and 12 "long" hours
of night at the winter solstice. Both are shown for latitude 45° N.

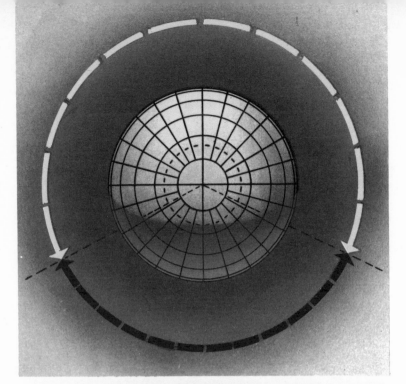

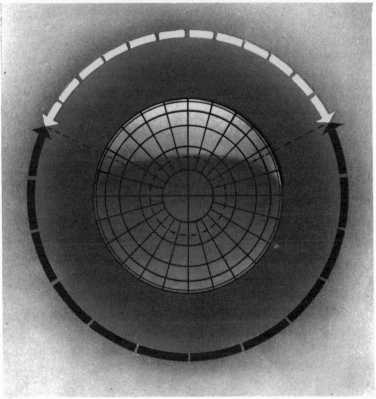

The seasons, northern hemisphere.

the year were the directions in which the sun rose and set. In step
with this annual cycle were the agricultural periods of sowing,
growth, ripening and harvesting. To reckon the agricultural, as
well as the religious activities, a calendar based on the solar year
of about 365 days was highly desirable. This was especially the
case in countries like Greece and Italy, where the seasons were
more distinct than those of Egypt and southern Mesopotamia.

In early times, and far more than today, the sun's diurnal course
was used to indicate the passage of time. Its progress in the sky
was reflected in the corresponding backward course of the shadow
of a stick or stone pillar stuck vertically in the ground. As early as
1400 B.C., and probably long before, the Egyptians used a small
wooden SHADOW-CLOCK, forerunner of the SUNDIAL. Reckoned
with reference to the sun, and for places well away from the
earth's equator, the twelve "hours" into which the interval sun-
rise-to-sunset was divided had a different length according to
the season, being longer in summer than in winter. Only at the
EQUINOXES on about March 21 and September 22 by modern
reckoning, did they equal in length the twelve hours of the night,
so that the joint period of day and night then contained twenty-

four equal hours. These EQUINOCTIAL HOURS, as the Greeks
called them, received full civil adoption only when mechanical
clocks came into general use, around the fifteenth century. For
early peoples, and even today in certain backward areas, hours
of equal length were not among the primary needs of life.

In addition to the uniform motion of the procession of stars
and the motion of the sun relative to the stars, the regular and
rapid progress of the moon in a west-to-east direction among the
stars made it an excellent arbiter of time. In about 27·32 days (a
SIDEREAL MONTH) the moon passes from a given star back again
to the same star (or nearly so), whereas the sun requires about
365 days (a SIDEREAL YEAR) to pursue a similar course. Once
every month, therefore, the moon appears to catch up with the
sun, overtake it, and pass right around the sky again in order to
repeat the process. Associated with this motion, and as if to
accentuate it, are the phases of the moon, the moon always being
a crescent when near the sun, and full when the two bodies are in
opposite parts of the sky. The lunar phase cycle, as was appreciated in ancient times, offers two further equal divisions of time,
one covering the "waxing moon" and the other, the "waning
moon". In addition, the cycle can be still more finely subdivided
into "quarters", each of approximately seven days.

For all early peoples the moon was a prominent and convenient
measure of time. Indeed, the LUNAR MONTH, along with the day,
appears to have been the earliest calendrical unit. Each month
was reckoned from the first appearance of the new moon in the
western sky. Unfortunately, the period new moon to new moon (a
LUNATION or SYNODICAL MONTH) is about 29 days 12 hours and
not a convenient 28 or 30 days. Twelve synodical months therefore
total approximately 354 days, or $11\frac{1}{4}$ days short of a SOLAR YEAR.

The Babylonians attempted to allow for this residual by introducing or "intercalating" an extra month once every two to three
solar years. The Hebrews operated their calendar on the basis
that 223 lunations were approximately 19 solar years. Hence at
the end of this period the Passover and other festivals, all fixed
with respect to the lunar months, repeated their seasonal incidence.
The Moslems made their year consist of twelve lunar months,

each with 30 days and 29 days alternately and altogether containing 354 days. The Moslem year therefore runs independent of the
solar year, with the result that a particular feast or period of fast-
ing, such as Ramadan, gradually moves through the seasons. The
Greeks and early Romans also used lunar calendars, but, despite
the periodic addition of extra days, failed to keep their religious
calendar in line with the seasons.

In ancient Egypt a solar calendar based on a year of 365 days
was an early institution. Twelve months of 30 days each made up
360 days, to which were added five extra days. Such a year, however, was found to be too short, for the various feasts and festivals
regulated by it arrived later by a quarter of a day every successive
calendar year.

The early history of astronomy is therefore largely the story of
man's struggle with the calendar, a struggle which stimulated observation of the sun, moon and stars and played a significant part
in the development of mathematics. As social life grew in complexity, it became increasingly evident that something more drastic than the old methods of calendrical adjustment was necessary.
In the Latin world the first calendrical reform of any consequence
was initiated by Julius Caesar. With the help of the mathematician
Sosigenes, Caesar drew up a system which ignored lunations
and had the solar year for its basis. After 45 B.C., and in accordance with the new reckoning, three years each with 365 days were
followed by a leap year with 366 days. The Roman calendar year
therefore contained 365¼ days divided among 12 months whose
arbitrarily-chosen lengths had no bearing whatever on the lunar
month. Even so, the Julian year was too long by some 11 minutes
14 seconds, and the vernal or spring equinox arrived earlier and
earlier at the rate of about one day every 120 years.

After the passage of several centuries it became apparent that
the date of the vernal equinox, and hence of Easter, was moving
too near the winter months. In 1582, when it arrived on March 11
instead of on March 21, Pope Gregory decreed that 10 days be
dropped out of the calendar. He also proposed a correction to the
JULIAN CALENDAR which required the omission of three leap
years in every 400 years and thereby reduced the difference be-

The world as imagined in ancient times, with the earth the center of all things.

tween the solar year and the average civil year to about one day
in 3,000 years. With its many imperfections, the GREGORIAN
CALENDAR, not adopted in England until 1752, now has wide-
spread usage.

Familiarity with the night sky reveals the interesting fact that
five of the brightest objects appear to wander slowly among the
others along quite complex paths. Although their general motions
are west-to-east, or direct, these wanderers, relative to the fixed
stars, periodically halt in their tracks, move for a time from east-
to-west, become stationary again, and then resume their direct
courses. The result is that they appear to trace out a series of loops
with respect to the background of stars.

These wanderers, known since antiquity, are the five planets
visible to the naked eye: Mercury, Venus, Mars, Jupiter, and
Saturn. Like planet earth they all revolve around the sun in nearly
circular paths or orbits. Both Mercury and Venus have ORBITS
smaller than the earth's; they therefore never appear far from the
vicinity of the sun. When furthest from the sun, about 47°, Venus
is a brilliant object, and is called the evening star when seen after
sundown and the morning star when seen before sunrise. Mars,
Jupiter, and Saturn, on the other hand, are superior planets in
that they move in orbits which lie outside the earth's orbit
around the sun. This explains how we can see them in parts of the
sky far removed from the sun's station. Early star-gazers noticed
the planetary loops but were unaware that they arise from differences between the different angular motions of the planets and of
the earth around the sun – that is, that they were watching the
planets from a moving earth.

The planets revolve around the sun in planes which are only
slightly inclined to the plane of the earth's orbit. As seen from the
earth, they, together with the moon, are always found close to the
annual path traced out by the sun, which is called the ECLIPTIC.
This means that the planets keep within the confines of a narrow
belt of the sky (called the ZODIAC or "circle of animals" by the
Greeks), a belt which from earliest times was divided into twelve
equal parts or signs. As seen from the sun, Mercury, the swiftest
planet, wanders once through the signs in an average time of 88

days, but slow-moving Saturn takes about 29½ years. There are three additional planets – Uranus, Neptune, and Pluto – which take longer than Saturn, but these were not discovered until after the TELESCOPE had been invented.

According to an age-old tradition, the priests of Babylonia and their successors, the Chaldeans, were highly skilled in astronomy. Yet of astronomy as a science, and apart from their work in determining time and drawing up calendars, they knew nothing. Only in later centuries, that is, after about the third century B.C., did the regular study of the motions of the sun, moon, and planets enable the Chaldeans to make predictions which, by the standards of those days could be called accurate. The ability of the priesthood to calculate in advance phenomena like ECLIPSES of the sun and moon and the various dispositions of the planets was confined to this later Chaldean period. At no time did the Chaldeans think in terms of a round earth or of the sun, moon and planets as objects moving in circular orbits in space.

The discipline of a *science* of the stars came from the ancient Greeks who in the early stages derived much of their practical knowledge about astronomy from the Near East. From PYTHA-GORAS, PLATO, and other philosophers came the idea that the earth is round and fixed immovably at the center of the celestial sphere or sphere of stars. Curiously enough the notion of a spherical earth appears to have arisen in the first instance not from observation but rather as a direct result of the Greek love of geometry. The circle, they argued, is the most perfect geometrical form; the sphere is the most perfect shape. Hence the earth must be spherical, as also are the heavens. The fact that circumpolar stars appear to move in circles around the NORTH CELESTIAL POLE undoubtedly added weight to the idea that the stars are fixed like luminous studs to an immense rotating crystal sphere. The concept of the celestial sphere is still retained by astronomers as a convenient fiction. It facilitates the description of the heavens on the earth-centered or GEOCENTRIC basis and provides a foundation for the whole elaborate structure of spherical astronomy.

The Greeks were bold and original thinkers. They attempted to reduce the entire physical universe or COSMOS to one geometrical model. Their concern was with broad issues, with the universe at large rather than with a detailed and direct study of any one part. In this sense they were cosmologists rather than astronomers. Their outlook was speculative rather than practical. For them the problems of astronomy were similar to those of geometry – one had just to sit down and work them out by means of the usual deductive procedures.

There were, however, exceptions to this attitude, although these did not appear until towards the end of the third century B.C. About 280 B.C., for example, ARISTARCHUS of Samos broke away from the cherished Greek idea that the earth is the center of the universe and that the heavens revolve around the earth. He suggested that the universe was sun-centered or heliocentric. This idea of a rotating and revolving earth seemed a curious and even dangerous departure from traditional thought, with the result that Aristarchus' theory failed to gain acceptance. By observations of the sun and moon he made a first attempt to determine their distances, but his method was incapable of giving accurate results. ERATOSTHENES, another Greek astronomer, attempted to measure the size of the earth. His method, sound in principle, consisted in measuring the midday lengths of shadows cast by vertical sundials at Alexandria and Syene, two places on almost the same meridian. He obtained a result which appears to have been close to that now accepted – an achievement which added further weight to the view that the earth is not only spherical but also very large by everyday standards.

The greatest Greek astronomer before the Christian era was HIPPARCHUS, who lived in the second century B.C. at Alexandria and Bithynia in Asia Minor. He was one of the first, if not the first to apply a yardstick to the heavens. His instruments, provided with circles divided into degrees and fitted with a simple sighting device, enabled him to determine angular separations between the stars with fair accuracy. For time determinations he used various kinds of sundial and CLEPSYDRA or water-clock.

Hipparchus drew up a catalogue of the positions of 1,080 stars. These he arranged in forty-eight constellations or "ASTER-ISMS" and described relative to the ecliptic, or apparent annual

The ancient Greeks considered the earth to be fixed in the middle of a rotating celestial sphere.

path of the sun. He also grouped the stars according to their brightness into six MAGNITUDES. The brightest stars were termed stars of the first magnitude, those a little less bright were of the second magnitude, and so on to those of the sixth magnitude, the faintest stars visible to the unaided eye. This classification was quite arbitrary, but it formed a useful basis for those which followed. The observation of a magnitude, combined with the belief that all the stars are at the same distance from the earth, led to the erroneous conclusion that a bright star is larger than a faint one.

By referring to earlier astronomical records, Hipparchus was able to investigate the earlier Babylonian discovery of the PRE-CESSION OF THE EQUINOXES. He compared his position of the bright star Spica in The Virgin with that found at an earlier period and realized that the star had moved eastward towards the autumnal equinox by about 2° in 150 years. This apparent motion, now fixed at 50·26″ a year, is shared by all the stars – they all move slowly eastward relative to the equinoxes. Precession, or the slow "wobble" of the earth's axis, also makes CELESTIAL POLES move round the corresponding poles of the ecliptic. The movement is so slow that it is completed only once in 25,800 years, and it means that the star Polaris, the star in the end of the tail of the Little Bear, is only temporarily the Pole Star. At present Polaris is just less than 1° from the North Celestial Pole and will be nearest to that point (just within 26′) in the year 2095. About 3000 B.C., when the Great Pyramid at Giza was built, the earth's north pole pointed fairly near the star Alpha Draconis, which then was the Pole Star. Some 12,000 years from now the bright star Vega will feature as the Pole Star.

Precession has to be taken into account in all work connected with the positions of celestial objects. Just as the position of a place on the earth can be defined in terms of the two co-ordinates latitude and longitude, so can an object in the heavens. The projection of the earth's equator on the sphere of stars is called the CELESTIAL EQUATOR, and an angular distance north or south of this is called the DECLINATION (Decl.). The Declination is therefore the celestial counterpart of terrestrial latitude. The second celestial co-ordinate, corresponding to terrestrial longitude, is

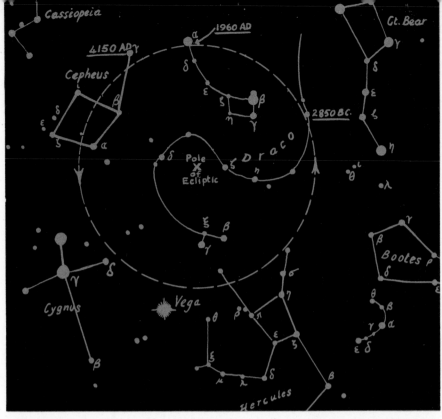

Precession causes the north celestial pole to move slowly among the stars. Its path is shown by the dotted circle which gives its position for 2850 B.C., the present (near Polaris), and for A.D. 4150.

The earth. likened to a spinning top, "wobbles" or "precesses" as it spins.

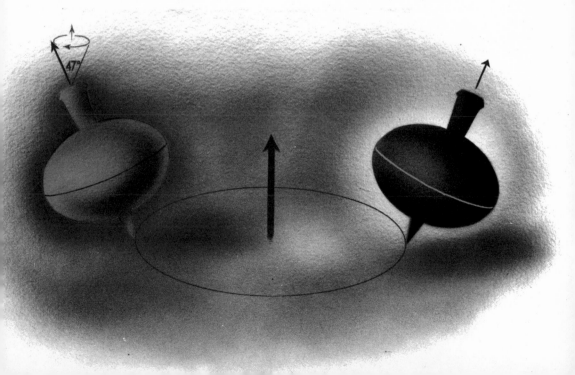

RIGHT ASCENSION (R.A.). It is measured eastward from the vernal equinox or first point of Aries and may be expressed in degrees, minutes, and seconds of arc, or in hours, minutes, and seconds of time. Since precession causes the equinox to move westward, the Right Ascension of all the stars is continuously increasing. It is therefore necessary always to specify the precise date or epoch when drawing up, for example, a catalogue of star positions in terms of R.A. and Decl.

The last great astronomer of ancient times was Claudius PTOLEMY, who worked at Alexandria in the second century A.D. He too made a survey of the stars, and his great book or *Syntax*, later known as the ALMAGEST, summarized the work of Hipparchus and the main Greek achievements in astronomy. So great was the importance of the *Almagest* that it remained the fundamental text for the study of astronomy for many centuries. In it we find the full flowering of the earth-centered or geocentric view of the cosmos. The earth, said Ptolemy, did not rotate, otherwise objects would be flung off its surface like mud from a spinning wheel. It remained at the center of all things because this was its natural place – it had no tendency to go either one way or the other. Around it and in successively larger spheres revolved the moon, Mercury, Venus, sun, Mars, Jupiter and Saturn, all of them deriving their motion from the motion of the immense and outermost sphere of FIXED STARS.

This general physical picture was Aristotelian, for it followed closely the pattern first set out by Aristotle in the fourth century B.C. Ptolemy, however, added geometrical refinements, using in this connection some of the ideas and observational findings of Hipparchus and retaining the notion of uniform motions in circular orbits. He used a most ingenious system to account for the non-uniform motions of the seven "wanderers". As each planet

Nicholas Copernicus taught that the earth and other planets revolved around the sun.

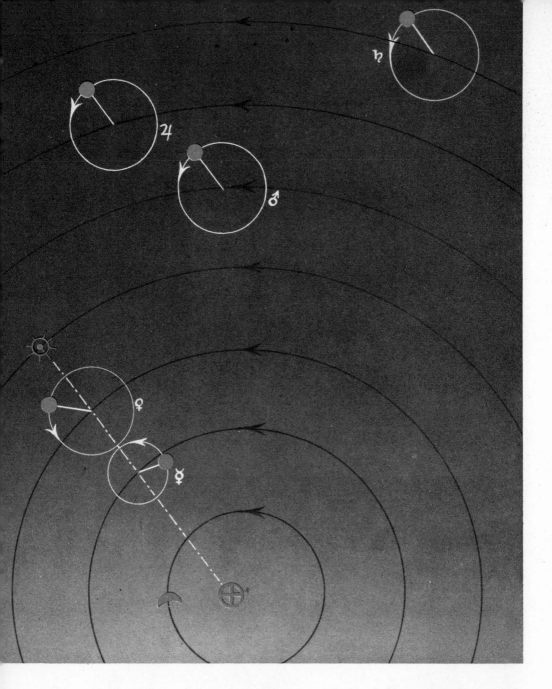

The Ptolemaic System. Each planet moves uniformly in a small circle (the epicycle) whose center orbits the earth on a circular track (the deferent). The actual motion of a planet is therefore a combination of two uniform circular motions. Only the sun and moon have no epicycles but move around on their deferents.

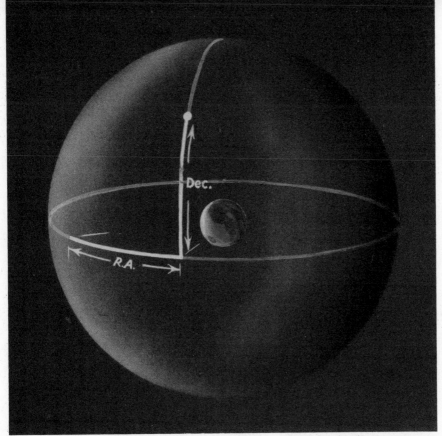

The position of a star on the celestial sphere in Right Ascension (R.A.) and Declination (Decl.) (*see* page 22).

moved in a small orbit or EPICYCLE so the center of the epicycle moved in a larger orbit or DEFERENT. The earth, moreover, was not necessarily placed at the center of this deferent, being shifted slightly to one side so that the deferent was an eccentric circle. Although the entire system, with its fixed earth and eighty component circles, was extremely complex, it served fairly well to predict the major observed motions of the sun, moon, and planets.

Among the Moslems, to whom we owe most of our star names, the *Almagest* was studied, commented upon, abridged, and modified with immense enthusiasm. This was the system of the heavens which became known to scholars in western Europe. It met its first great challenge from Nicholas Kopernik, better known as COPERNICUS, a canon in the cathedral city of Frauenburg. In

Tycho Brahe.

1543, and in his great work *De Revolutionibus Orbium Coelestium*, Copernicus, like Aristarchus, suggested that appearances in the wheeling heavens could be described more economically by transferring some of the motion to the earth itself. Why, for instance, say that the entire sphere of stars rotates when the same effect can be produced by giving the earth a daily rotation? Why make the sun and planets all revolve around the earth when the same appearances can the more simply be produced by having the earth revolve around the sun? And what better object could we have at the center of the universe than the sun, a body known to be larger than the earth and one which illuminates the whole at once? "So the sun sits", Copernicus wrote, "as upon a royal throne ruling his children the planets which circle round him."

This proposed change in viewpoint came as a great shock to most of Copernicus' contemporaries, for they disliked the idea of giving the earth so undignified a position. Yet when put to practical test the theory was found to account for the appearances in the heavens far more simply than and yet just as accurately as did the more involved theory of Ptolemy.

In 1572 there came another great step away from traditional thought. A "new" star or SUPERNOVA blazed out in the constellation of Cassiopeia and was shown by the Danish astronomer, TYCHO BRAHE, to be located among the fixed stars. Hitherto it was thought that no change of any kind could take place above the sphere of the moon – that the sphere of stars was both perfect and unchanging. Then in 1577 a bright COMET appeared, which Tycho Brahe and others found by measurement to be moving at a distance greater than that of the moon. Aristotle and others had taught that comets, like "shooting stars" or METEORS, were events in the earth's atmosphere, but it now became evident that they deserved planetary status.

After observing the new star, Tycho Brahe devoted the rest of his life to the accurate determination of the positions and motions of the heavenly bodies. At his observatory at Uraniborg on the island of Hveen he assembled a princely collection of large measuring instruments of his own design. For 25 years he diligently measured the position of the stars, and used these positions

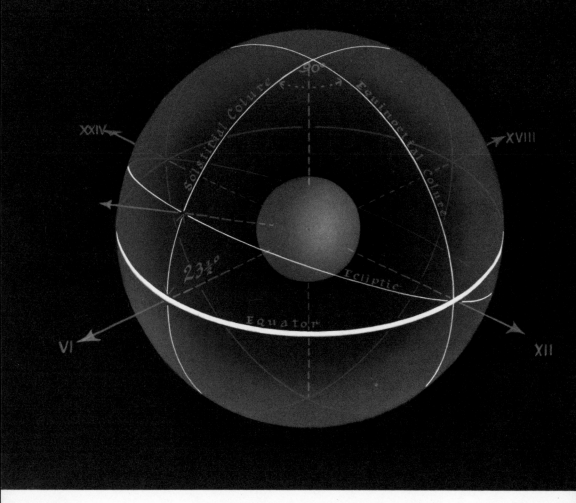

The main great circles of the celestial sphere.

as reference points for tracing the paths of the moon and five planets. For the first time for many centuries, at least in the Western World, the problems of astronomy were set by the accurate observation of the heavens themselves.

In 1609 a Dutch spectacle maker named Hans LIPPERSHEY succeeded in making the first telescope. News of the invention soon reached Galileo GALILEI, professor of mathematics at Padua, who promptly made one for his own use. He turned it to the moon and saw that the moon's surface, far from being smooth and polished as Aristotle had taught, was rough with mountains, CRATERS and valleys. Nor was the sun a perfect globe. The telescope revealed that it was blemished with spots – dark spots that drifted across the brilliant disk and indicated that the sun, like the earth, spins on an axis. The MILKY WAY, whose nature had hitherto been a complete mystery, was found to be made up of innumerable stars; the planet Venus was seen to go through a cycle of phases; Jupiter appeared round and was accompanied by four moons. Finding that a moving body such as Jupiter had other bodies moving round it, he concluded that the earth, or even the sun, was not the only center of motion.

As a result of these discoveries, Galileo wrote strongly in praise of the theory of Copernicus, thereby incurring the displeasure of the Church. On 22 June 1633, he was persuaded by the Inquisition of renounce his heretical opinions after which he was placed under virtual house-arrest at Siena and in his villa at Arcetri. Yet in spite of these proceedings, Galileo's exciting discoveries with the new instrument could not be ignored. For the first time man was not wholly dependent on the naked-eye observation of the heavens.

The final break with the age-old notion of circular planetary orbits came as a result of the work of Johannes KEPLER. For a brief period at Prague, Kepler assisted Tycho Brahe in the reduction of the latter's planetary observations. After Tycho's death in 1601, Kepler used the recorded observations for a special study of Mars. Not until 1609 did he succeed in finding that they best fitted a planet which moved in an elliptical orbit and according to a precise mathematical rule. This discovery he expressed in the form of two laws, the so-called First and Second Laws of Kepler. In modern form they state that:

(1) Each planet revolves round the sun in an ellipse with the sun at one of the foci.

(2) Each planet moves so that a line drawn from it to the sun covers equal areas in equal times.

Ten years later, in 1619, Kepler stated that he had found another or Third Law to the effect that:

(3) The squares of the periods of revolution of the planets round the sun are proportional to the cubes of mean distances.

The next great step forward was made between 1665 and 1687

Galileo Galilei.

by Isaac NEWTON. From the observation of a falling apple, Newton was led to investigate the force or forces which make the
moon go round the earth and speed the planets and comets on
their precise paths. He concluded that the force which causes un-
supported objects to fall to the ground operates throughout the
far reaches of interplanetary space and even, as was shown later,
of interstellar space. This force is the force of gravity which con-
forms to a law now usually stated as follows:

"Every particle of matter in the universe attracts every other
particle with a force which varies inversely as the square of the
distance between them and directly as the product of the masses
of the particles."

The planets, Newton showed, move in accordance with Kepler's Laws as a direct result of the Law of GRAVITATION, and
the Law of INERTIA, stated earlier by Galileo.

With the aid of the Law of Gravitation, and with remarkable mathematical skill and insight. Newton disclosed the principles of celestial mechanics. These he employed to explain the ebb and flow of the tides, and showed that the rise and fall of the water is a direct consequence of the attractive force of the moon and to a lesser degree, of the sun also. He made a study of the precession of the equinoxes, and by dynamical considerations showed that it is brought about by the attractive forces which the sun and moon exercise on the equatorial bulge of the earth. He also studied the irregularities in the motion of the moon which occur because the attraction of the sun on the moon varies as the moon moves around the earth. The moon is therefore subject to perturbations; it does not move exactly in an ELLIPSE, nor is the earth exactly in one focus of this ellipse. Newton also explored the effects of the planetary pulls on each other which produce small changes in their motions.

Newton even extended his system of celestial mechanics to embrace comets, thereby enabling Edmond HALLEY to predict that the great comet of 1682 would return either at the end of 1758 or the beginning of 1759. Halley was aware that the perturbations of Jupiter and Saturn might slightly alter the time of the comet's reappearance, as proved to be the case, for the comet was not seen until January, 1759. Its appearance according to prediction was another triumph for Newtonian mechanics, already being extended to cope with further details of the motions of the moon

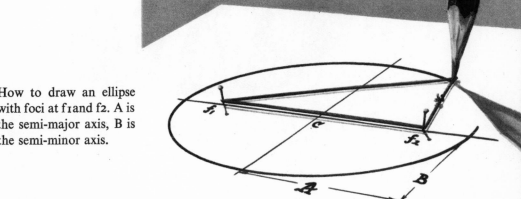

How to draw an ellipse with foci at f1 and f2. A is the semi-major axis, B is the semi-minor axis.

and planets. By that time the break with the old Ptolemaic system was complete. Not only did Newtonian mechanics describe accurately the motions of the moon and planets, but James BRADLEY in 1782 had demonstrated the earth's motion round the sun by an independent astronomical method.

There remained one major problem, the measurement of the distances of the stars, regarded as being immensely great from quite early times. This was not resolved until 1838, when the German astronomer, Freidrich Wilhelm BESSEL, published the results of his measurements of the star 61 Cygni. Its distance came out at about half a million times that of the sun from the earth – yet this star was one of the nearest of the stars. It appeared that Thomas DIGGES, an ardent Copernican, did not greatly err when in 1576 he wrote that "This orbe of starres fixed infinitely up extendeth itself in altitude sphericallye ... garnished with perpetuall shininge glorious lightes innumerable farr excellinge our sonne both in quantitye and qualitye."

The sun as a god (*see* pages 9 and 10).

2. The tools of astronomy

Astronomy is a unique science in the sense that we cannot as yet travel to other worlds and thereby study them at close quarters or bring back samples to analyse in the laboratory. So far our knowledge of the heavens has been based on the messages contained in light, that mysterious agent which crosses the vast reaches of space and links us with the distant stars. For the layman this is perhaps the most fascinating yet perplexing aspect of astronomy. Granted that we can see the stars, and granted that light is the go-between that enables us to see them, yet how can astronomers from the study of light alone determine the distances, sizes, temperatures and natures of the stars? How is it possible to wrest so many secrets from what is, to all intents and purposes, a narrow beam of starlight? To answer these questions we shall first consider the nature and behavior of light and then proceed to show how astronomers unravel and interpret its message.

Any answer to the question "What is light?" must of necessity involve physical and psychical considerations. On the physical side we can think of light as luminous energy which travels from external objects to the observer. When this energy enters the eye through the pupil it is focused on a delicate receptor membrane called the retina. It is there converted into nervous energy and as such travels to the brain where it gives rise to the sensation of vision. Our concern here will be only with the physical aspect of the process, that is, with what is taking place between the source and the observer. In this connection the astronomer, in accordance with his particular requirements, chooses to think of light in terms of RAYS, waves and PHOTONS.

"A ray", wrote Newton, "is the least part of light." Imagine, for example, that we can narrow down a beam of sunlight until it becomes a mere thread. The narrowest imaginable thread could then be termed a ray; narrow it further and both ray and light disappear. It is also known that light normally travels in straight lines. Hence when we consider the geometrical aspects of light, a ray is represented by a straight line, but like a circle or any other line, it is a geometrical abstraction. Astronomers find it extremely convenient to represent light in this way, especially when they are discussing the design and function of telescopes and other such instruments.

The first telescopes were based on the fact that if we hold a concave LENS close to the eye and look through it and a more distant convex lens, remote objects are seen the correct way up and magnified. This particular combination of two lenses is known as the "Galilean" telescope. In normal use the two lenses are separated by the sum of their FOCAL LENGTHS. Then the ratio of the focal length of the convex lens to that of the concave lens is the apparent magnifying power of the telescope.

The convex lens or OBJECT-GLASS must therefore have a focal length several times greater than that of the concave lens or eyepiece – at least if useful magnification is required. Its function is to collect light from distant objects and to condense the rays into a small image in its focal plane. This image is then magnified by the eye lens. One of the largest of Galileo's telescopes, now preserved in Florence, magnifies about 20 times and is some 4 feet long. Owing to the difficulty of obtaining good images with big lenses, the effective aperture of the object-glass is no more than two-thirds of an inch in diameter.

Top: sunlight (white light) passes through a hole in the wall of a darkened room. It is then dispensed by a glass prism to form a multicolored patch or "impure" spectrum. *Lower:* when the sunlight passes first through a narrow slit and then through a glass prism and condensing lens it forms a regular sequence of colors known as a "pure" spectrum.

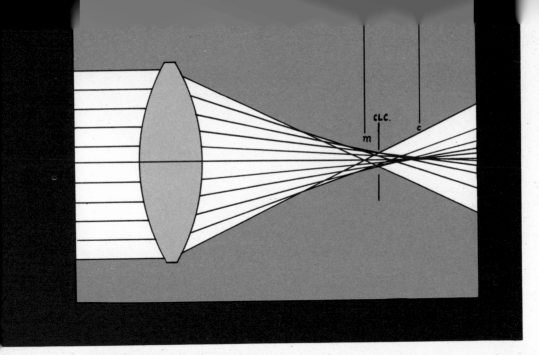

Spherical aberration. Rays incident near the edge of a convex lens come to focus sooner than those incident near the center. The line C L C marks the area of "least confusion".

In an attempt to increase the performance and the magnifying power of telescopes, many opticians and astronomers in the seventeenth century made object-glasses longer and longer in focal length. Johann HEVELIUS, of Danzig, observed the moon and planets with telescopes as long as 150 feet. Christian HUYGENS discovered Titan (the largest satellite of Saturn) and also the rings of Saturn with the aid of 23-foot and 123-foot telescopes, and one astronomer planned making telescopes as long as 300 and 600 feet in the hope of seeing animals on the moon.

These long refracting telescopes were extremely unwieldy, the more so since they were often hoisted aloft and guided by ropes and pulleys attached to a high pole. Furthermore, the area of the sky that could be seen at one time was very small. Even so, they provided a good range of magnification, and also minimized the effects of false color or CHROMATIC ABERRATION, one of the most serious defects of any two-lens refracting telescope. Another defect of all such simple telescopes is SPHERICAL ABERRATION, or the inability of an ordinary lens with spherical surfaces to bring all of a beam of parallel light rays to one common point FOCUS. Owing to these two aberrations, objects seen through early telescopes contained false color and could not be brought into sharp focus.

In an effort to improve the behavior of ordinary lenses, Newton undertook original work in optics, investigating, among other things, the SPECTRUM or colored band formed when sunlight is passed through a glass PRISM. After a masterly series of experiments he concluded that white light or sunlight is not pure or homogenous light but consists of parts, each of which undergoes a particular bending or refraction by the prism. Differences in the amount of this refraction for different colors disperses light into the spectrum band of colors. Newton described this in terms of rays; violet-producing rays, for example, are rays which undergo greater deviation by the prism than do red-producing rays. To explain these and many other observations Newton proposed a corpuscular theory. Light, he suggested, consisted of small bodies emitted in all directions from shining bodies. To fit the observations, such light particles must speed up when they pass from air to glass and water. Later experiments showed, on the contrary, that light travels more slowly in glass and water than in air, and Newton's theory had to be rejected.

Nowadays we describe the dispersion of light in terms of a WAVE THEORY. Light is regarded as a continuous train of transverse waves or vibrations of ELECTROMAGNETIC ENERGY. These vibrations form WAVE-FRONTS which spread out from a source like the ripples produced when a stone is thrown into still water, except that they do not lengthen as they advance. They are so small that the WAVELENGTH or distance from crest to crest, is only about two millionths of an inch, with the waves of violet light being only about half as long as those of red light. The wave-fronts and the light energy associated with them travel through space at the immense speed of 186,283 miles a second, or very nearly 300,000 kilometers a second.

Newton thought that whenever light is bent or refracted by glass it is also dispersed by a corresponding amount. He therefore despaired of ever freeing the refracting telescope from false color effects. In 1668 he made his first reflecting telescope. In this instrument, light from distant objects is collected not by a convex lens but by a concave mirror. Placed at the bottom of an open tube, the mirror reflects the incident light to form an image at the top of the tube. Not only is the image free from chromatic aberration, but if the mirror has a paraboloidal surface it is also corrected for spherical aberration. To view the image directly the observer would need to have the eyepiece (and hence place his head) over the mouth of the tube, but this would block out much of the incident light. This difficulty Newton surmounted by inserting a small flat mirror across the cone of reflected rays. The rays are thereby reflected through an opening in the side of the tube into an eyepiece directed at right angles to the optical axis of the concave mirror.

Newton appears to have made two small reflecting telescopes, but only one now exists. This made its first public appearance in London at the meeting of the ROYAL SOCIETY on January 11, 1672, and was examined with great interest by the assembled company which included King Charles II. With its concave spherical mirror of only $1\frac{1}{3}$ inches diameter and focal length $12\frac{1}{2}$ inches, it magnified 35 times and was capable of showing the larger craters on the moon and the four satellites of Jupiter discovered by Galileo.

Although Newton has the credit of being the first to make a satisfactory reflecting telescope, others preceded him in the consideration of mirror systems. In the previous century, Leonard DIGGES appears to have suggested and even used combinations of concave and convex mirrors to see distant objects magnified. In 1636, Marin MERSENNE, a Minorite friar, proposed combining two concave PARABOLOIDS for this purpose. Then James GREGORY, successively professor of mathematics of St Andrews and Edinburgh, discussed in 1663 a form of reflecting telescope since called the "Gregorian", though apparently Gregory never made such a telescope.

The Gregorian system is similar in design to one proposed by Mersenne in that the beam reflected up the tube by the concave paraboloid is reflected down again by a small secondary mirror which has its surface figured to a concave ELLIPSOID. To gain access to the final image, the primary mirror has a central hole

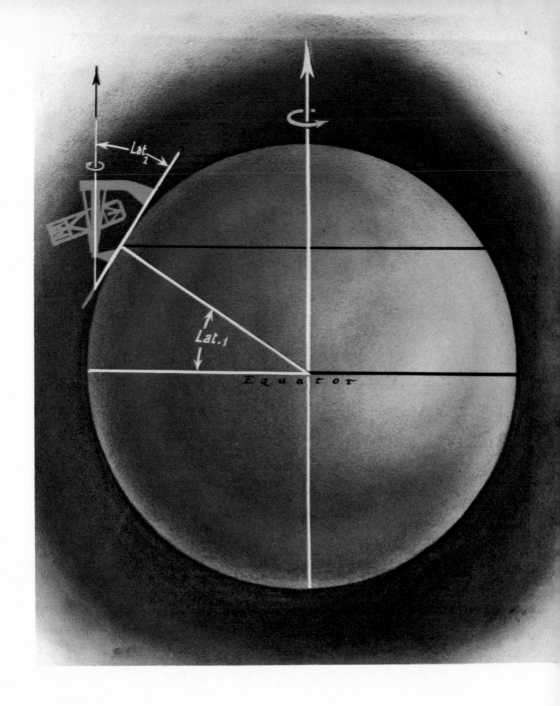

In order to follow a star conveniently a telescope has to be mounted so that it can rotate on a polar axis. This axis must be parallel to the axis of the earth.

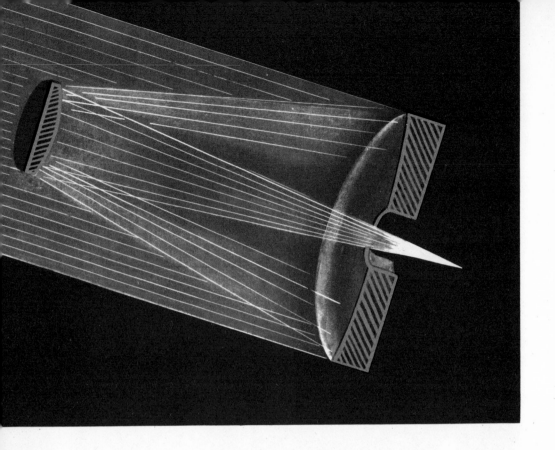

The Cassegrain reflecting telescope.

into which the eyepiece tube fits. Gregory's reflector is therefore a mirror version of Kepler's refractor, and like the latter can be pointed directly to the object under observation. It also has the advantage of yielding erect images and is therefore suitable for the observation of terrestrial objects.

Mersenne also proposed a third variant of a two-mirror system, in which the secondary mirror was a convex HYPERBOLOID. This was subsequently reintroduced by Guillaume CASSEGRAIN about 1761, and is now known as the "Cassegrain" system. The three different types of reflecting telescope – the Gregorian, Newtonian and Cassegrain – were therefore each invented by different persons within the narrow compass of ten years.

Gregory emphasized the fact that his system is free from spherical aberration only so long as the two mirrors are given aspherical surfaces. At the time, neither he nor the London master-opticians whom he employed could produce well-polished spherical surfaces, let alone more complex forms, and his design was temporarily shelved.

Optical mirrors were then made from discs of speculum metal, a copper-tin alloy of great hardness capable of taking a polish similar to that of burnished silver. Newton made his mirrors of this metal, grinding them with emery and polishing them with putty powder embedded in pitch. Done without a machine the work was slow and arduous, and opticians at first found it almost impossible to give the finished surface a uniform polish. But as the rough observation and experience of early trials gave way to set procedures and craftsmanship, a few master-opticians began to exploit the need for good-quality reflecting telescopes of moderate aperture. First and foremost in this lucrative field was James SHORT, who in 1740 set up a workshop near the Strand in London. Most of his telescopes were Gregorians. They ranged in size from small hand instruments to giants (for those days) of 18 inches aperture and 12 feet focus.

As an instrument of discovery the Newtonian far excelled the others. This was due primarily to the outstanding labors of William HERSCHEL. Finding good telescopes expensive and difficult to obtain, Herschel made his own and used them to make a series of systematic surveys of the stars. During the comparatively brief period of sixteen years (1773–89). Herschel progressed from Newtonian-type reflectors of 6 inches aperture to a giant of 48 inches aperture and 40 feet focal length. Thereafter the Newtonian and not the Gregorian became the accepted system for research in sidereal astronomy, and in point of size progressed through the 72-inch giant of William Parsons, Lord ROSSE at Parsonstown, Ireland, to the 100-inch Hooker telescope at Mount Wilson, California. The largest reflector is the 200-inch Hale on Palomar Mountain. This is a compound system; it can be used either for direct focus photography or for photography and spectography at one of two alternative Cassegrain foci.

Newton's hasty generalization that refraction is always accompanied by comparable dispersion went unchallenged until 1755.

In that year, Chester Moor HALL, a barrister with scientific interests, introduced a compound convex lens, which, contrary to Newton's teaching, could form images of distant objects with little trace of false color. Hall used two different types of glass, combining a convex lens of crown glass with a concave lens of flint glass so that the chromatic aberration of one lens almost neutralized that of the other. He had in mind telescopes fitted with this kind of lens (later called an ACHROMATIC or "no-color" lens)

The 200-inch Hale reflecting telescope.

John Dollond.

for their object-glasses, but the London opticians whom he approached showed little interest in the proposal. In consequence, only two or three achromatic telescopes were ever made to his specification.

Twenty-five years later the London optician John DOLLOND re-invented the achromatic lens, and in collaboration with his son Peter began to market achromatic telescopes. Hall's principle as applied by the Dollonds made new instruments of the telescope and MICROSCOPE. By 1800, surveying instruments and astronomical measuring instruments were being fitted with achromatic telescopes. By the end of the nineteenth century, a large number of achromatic refracting telescopes ranging upwards in size to one of 40 inches aperture were in regular use in astronomical observatories.

The two largest refractors are the 36-inch at the Lick Observa-

The principle of the astronomical refracting telescope.

tory of the University of California and the 40-inch of the Yerkes
Observatory of the University of Chicago. Both object-glasses are
the work of the famous American telescope-makers Alvan CLARK
and Sons and were completed in 1888 and 1897 respectively. The
mountings were designed and made by Warner and Swasey, two
engineers who collaborated with the Clarks in producing some of
the largest refracting telescopes in the United States. Both instruments are still in regular use and in addition to visual observations
have been adapted for photographic work.

One of the most powerful tools of modern astronomy is the
photographic plate. Its great value lies in the fact that unlike the
human eye an exposed photographic plate can store up the light
impressions it receives. It gives a permanent record of objects so
faint that they cannot be seen by the most sensitive eye behind the
largest of telescopes. This means that the measurement and discussion of a few plates taken under good observing conditions
and with the minimum of observing time can provide weeks of
work in the laboratory. A large telescope is therefore used to the
greatest possible advantage – it is able to give maximum results in
minimum time.

Photography now has such wide application in astronomy that

except for studies of the physical features of the moon and planets, the use of the telescope as a visual instrument has almost ceased. Sunspots are recorded daily by photography, while CORONA-GRAPHS at high-altitude observatories permit the direct photo-graphy of the sun's inner CORONA – a feature hitherto seen only during the fleeting minutes of a total solar eclipse. Photographs of the moon reveal more and more detail with every improvement in photographic plates. Many thousand stars may simultaneously record themselves on a single photographic plate and counts of their numbers facilitate statistical studies in stellar distribution.

Stellar PHOTOMETRY developed greatly through the intercomparison of photographic image sizes and densities. Plate measurements of star PARALLAX displacements have now superseded all other direct methods for the trigonometrical determination of stellar distances.

Photographic methods have even invaded MERIDIAN astronomy. Considerable attention has recently been given to improved methods of time-keeping and time-checking, the more so since a clock with a quartz-crystal can keep time to within 0·001 of a second a day. A fairly recent development is the PHOTO-GRAPHIC ZENITH TELESCOPE which yields results far greater in accuracy than any obtained by traditional visual means.

The successes of astronomical photography would not have

The 40-inch refracting telescope of the Yerkes Observatory.

been possible without several important improvements in instru-
mentation. One of these was the introduction in the mid-nineteenth century of the silver-on-glass mirror. In 1856 the German
chemist Justus von LIEBIG found that he could by chemical
means coat a polished glass surface with a perfectly continuous
film of pure silver. Jean Bernard Léon FOUCAULT in France,
George H. WITH and George CALVER in England, and Henry
DRAPER in America all pioneered in the development of glass
mirrors. They realized at once that silver-coated mirrors offered
many advantages over their metal counterparts. A glass surface
is far more easily worked than one on metal and the glass itself is
much lighter in weight. The silver film is easily applied and,
although it tarnishes, can be replaced without interfering in any
way with the mirror's shape. Mirrors of speculum metal also
tarnished, but their reflectivity could be restored only by completely reworking the optical surface – a long and arduous under-
taking when it concerned mirrors as large as 48 and 72 inches in
diameter. The mirrors of most modern giant reflectors are made
of pyrex, a glass with a low COEFFICIENT OF EXPANSION and high
THERMAL DIFFUSIVITY, at least when compared with ordinary
glass. They are also now coated with aluminium by a vacuum
technique, because aluminium films are far more durable than
those of silver.

Large mirrors, no less than small ones, have to be accurately
worked and figured so that every ray in the light from a star is
brought to a point focus. In practice, and however perfect may be
the paraboloidal form of the mirror's surface, star images are not
points but small disks of light. These disks are in part accounted
for in terms of DIFFRACTION. That is to say, the light waves coming from the star are "bent" or diffracted by the circular edge of
the mirror and also by the edges of any obstacles such as the
secondary mirror and its supports. The effects of diffraction,
being an inevitable consequence of the waveform nature of light,
can be minimized but never eliminated. They are larger for telescopes of small aperture and long focal length (small aperture
ratio) than for those of large aperture and short focal length
(large aperture ratio).

The star disks, or AIRY DISKS as they are often called, are further enlarged and at the same time made more diffuse by tremors and currents in the air which cause the stars to "twinkle". Between a large primary mirror and the photographic plate of a reflecting telescope there can be all manner of optical irregularities, the effect of which, added to those produced by turbulence in the earth's atmosphere, turns the Airy Disk into a small fuzzy blob with indefinite boundaries. One way of avoiding this would be to escape altogether from the earth's atmosphere in an earth satellite, or transport the telescope piecemeal to a base on the moon and there assemble and operate it in a vacuum.

The smallest photographic star images are undoubtedly those produced by Schmidt-type systems. In its basic form, and as first made by Bernhard SCHMIDT in 1930, the Schmidt system contains only two optical elements. The image-forming element is a spherical concave mirror which has at its center of curvature an aspherical "lens" or plate so shaped that it eliminates the spherical aberration of the concave mirror. The photographic plate is

The principle of the Schmidt Photographic Telescope.

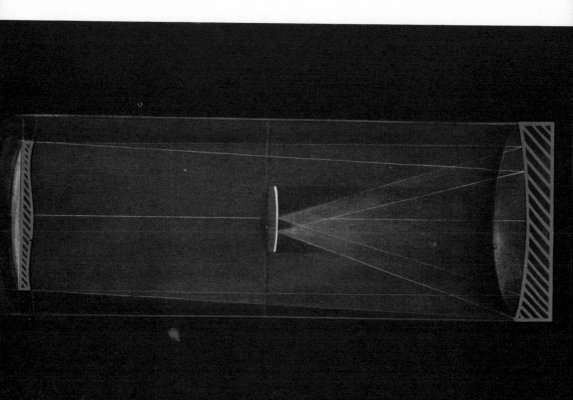

mounted in the center of the tube midway between the mirror and corrector plate, and must be bent to a curved shape. In an alternative arrangement, introduced in 1941 by D. D. Maksutov of Moscow and independently by Albert Bouwers of Delft, the corrector takes the form of a zero-power MENISCUS LENS with spherical surfaces. Both the Schmidt and Bouwers-Maksutov systems can be made in Cassegrain and Gregorian forms, and James G. Baker and others have produced several variations of the Schmidt design.

As a tool of astronomy the Schmidt system is valuable because it is photographically rapid. The focal length of the primary mirror of the 200-inch telescope is 660 inches, so that the primary focus permits direct photography at a maximum aperture-ratio of 660/200 or f/3·3. Critical definition, however, is restricted to the central part of the plate owing to yet another aberration known as "COMA". Stars at the edges of the plate have a slightly pear-shaped appearance, although this can be corrected in part by placing a special lens over the plate. A Schmidt system, on the other hand, can reproduce stars over a large area as neat tiny disks, so tiny in fact that on some plates the disks are quite invisible to the unaided eye.

The largest Schmidt telescope is that on Palomar Mountain. The corrector element is 48 inches in diameter. The spherical mirror, at the bottom of the 20-foot long tube, has a diameter of 72 inches. The system works at f/2·6 and is used solely for photography with plates 14 inches square.

Thanks to recent developments in electronics, and in particular in the design and construction of photo-multiplier tubes, astronomers can measure the brightness of a star to within a single hundredth of a magnitude. In sensitivity a PHOTO-ELECTRIC PHOTOMETER can surpass the best photographic plates, but whereas a plate covers a whole field of stars, the photo-electric photometer can deal with only a tiny part of the sky, or better, with one star at a time. The photographic limit of the 200-inch telescope is about magnitude 23·5, but a photo-electric pulse counter used with that telescope can reach down to magnitude 25·0. The main difficulty in going fainter than the photographic threshold lies in locating stars and systems of stars (GALAXIES) to observe.

It may be thought that a photographic plate needs only to be exposed long enough in the primary focal plane of the 200-inch telescope to record even the very faintest stars. This is unfortunately not the case. Experience with this instrument shows that blue-sensitive plates exposed longer than 30 minutes are so fogged that no additional faint star images can be recorded. The diffuse background glow of the night sky sets a definite limit to the faintness of a star observable by either photographic or photo-electric methods, and quite regardless of more rapid optical systems and more sensitive photographic emulsions.

One way of reducing the effect of sky glow and image blur due to atmospheric turbulence is to reduce exposure times by using an image converter. A few years ago A. Lallemand and M. Duchesne obtained encouraging results with an elaborate electro-photographic technique applied to a large refractor at the Paris Observatory. A photosensitive surface sealed in a vacuum tube was placed in the primary image plane of the object-glass and ejected ELECTRONS in proportion to the light distribution over its surface. These were focused directly on a suitably sensitized plate as used in nuclear research which served as the electrical ANODE. Well-defined impressions of Saturn were obtained in only one-fifth of a second and stars normally photographed in 3 minutes were recorded in 5 seconds. In an alternative arrangement, now being developed, the electrons are focused on a luminescent screen either directly or after multiple-stage amplification by a series of electron multipliers.

At the 1955 meeting of the International Astronomical Union in Dublin, an experimental television device was applied to a 12-inch refractor. In this case electrons were accelerated and focused on a plate which was scanned electronically, and the picture was shown on a standard TV screen. The arrangement gave a light boost of about 100 and a corresponding decrease in exposure time – and without any noticeable loss in definition. Essentially the same method was tried at the Lowell Observatory, Arizona. A 24-inch refractor formed a 10·5 millimeter image of Mars on the

CATHODE of an ORTHICON TUBE and permitted photography through a red filter with an exposure time of as little as one fifteenth of a second.

It must be stressed that the image converters or light amplifiers so far developed intensify both the picture *and* its background. The gain in image size and brightness is not accompanied by any corresponding increase in detail. At the present rate of progress, however, it should soon be possible to record details of large-scale planetary images by this means, using of course those all-too-rare moments of "good seeing" or optimum definition.

If we restrict ourselves to the visual and photographic aspects of the heavenly bodies, we restrict our knowledge of them to that which comes from only a small part of the total available radiation. The wavelength band which gives rise to vision is a tiny section of the total range of wavelengths known as the ELECTRO-MAGNETIC SPECTRUM. The violet end of the visual spectrum leads to the ULTRA-VIOLET and the red end to the INFRA-RED, both of which can be reached by dyed photographic plates and photoelectric photometers. Even so, the total range covered by these means is a very restricted one, owing, simply, to the earth's atmosphere. Water vapor and fine dust particles in the atmosphere absorb all but the longest waves of the ultra-violet and the shortest waves of the infra-red. It would therefore seem that as long as we remain at the bottom of earth's ocean of air our view of the stellar universe will be limited by the restrictions of the "optical window".

Fortunately there is another gap, the "radio window", through which come waves which range in wavelength from a few centimeters to about 20 meters. To collect these waves astronomers use various types of radio telescopes, all of which have an optical basis. In one of these the waves are collected by a steerable paraboloidal dish and focused on the antenna of a small aerial. The largest radio telescope of this kind is the 250-foot paraboloid of the Jodrell Bank Experimental Station near Manchester, England, but even larger instruments are being built. Yet despite its immense size the Jodrell telescope has a resolving power far below that of even the smallest optical telescope. Resolving power is

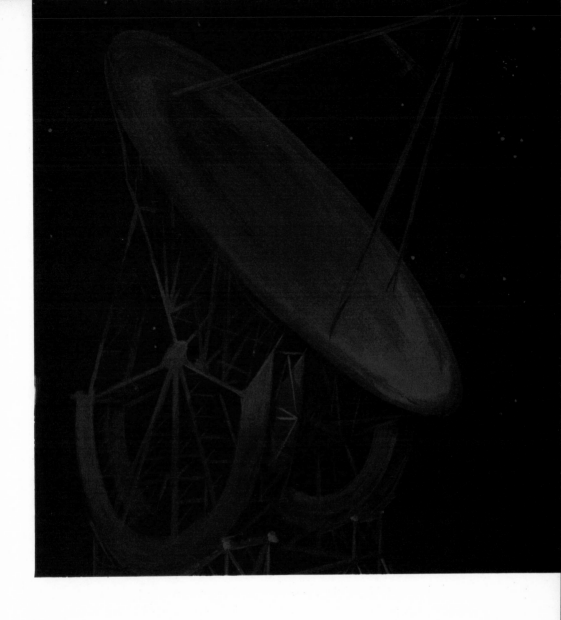

Artist's impression of the 600-foot radio-telescope at Green Bank, West Virginia.

akin to beam width, or the angle of the cone in which the radio waves are received, which depends on the ratio of the wave length to the diameter of the "mirror". Its value for an optical telescope is a mere fraction of a second of arc, but that for a 250-foot paraboloid tuned to receive on a wavelength of 1 meter is about 1°. In another type of radio telescope, known as an interferometer and used with great success to detect discrete radio sources or "radio stars", the collecting elements consist of two well-spaced but connected aerial systems. All types can, of course, be operated continuously in all weathers, for radio waves are not affected by daylight, mist, fog, or clouds.

Before 1931, when the American engineer Karl Jansky first detected the radio waves which come from interstellar regions, astronomers were wholly dependent on the views obtained through the "optical window". How well they exploited this to learn about the physics of heavenly bodies will be seen when we turn to consider the findings of ASTROPHYSICS. Many of these are a direct consequence of work done with the ASTRONOMICAL SPECTRO-GRAPH, an instrument whose origins lie in the first years of the nineteenth century.

When Newton formed a spectrum by passing a beam of sunlight through a glass prism he found that it consisted of a series of overlapping colored patches. A spectrum of this kind is called an impure spectrum. Its purity was greatly increased by the German optician Joseph von FRAUNHOFER, who in 1814 passed sunlight first through a narrow slit and then viewed the slit through a small telescope in front of which was fixed a glass prism. On looking into the telescope, Fraunhofer saw that the sun's spectrum was crossed by a number of fine dark lines.

These lines owe their presence to selective absorption in the sun's atmosphere. If the sun were a white-hot solid body, like the filament of an electric light, the solar spectrum would be a continuous band of color; light of every wavelength from violet to deep red would be present. The fact is that the sun has a tenuous atmosphere of glowing gases which are at a temperature generally lower than those in deeper regions. ATOMS of each chemical element in this gas absorb certain narrow wavebands of the

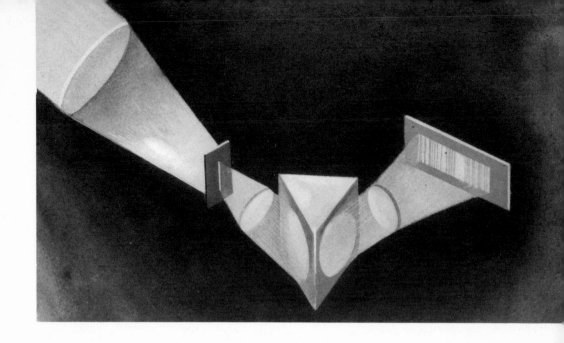

The Spectrograph.

original outward moving radiation and in so doing produce distinctive gaps or lines in the spectrum. The atoms cannot retain the absorbed energy, but quickly re-emit it in all directions. Some is emitted sideways to the original light and some even starts back towards the sun. The observed dark lines are not black, but only dark in comparison to the unabsorbed colors nearby. By comparing the positions of these dark lines with those given by glowing gases in the laboratory, astronomers are able to ascertain the nature and chemical composition of the sun's atmosphere.

Similar absorption lines in the spectra of stars reveal the interesting fact that the stars are comparable in their natures and materials to the sun. In order to obtain a record of a star's spectrum the starlight is focused on the slit of a spectrograph by the object-glass or mirror system of a telescope. The slit lies in the focal plane of a COLLIMATING LENS which feeds the starlight as a parallel beam to one or more glass prisms. The dispersed light is then collected by a small telescope (to complete a SPECTROSCOPE) or by the lens of a camera (to complete a spectrograph).

One other characteristic of light permits astronomers to tease from it much additional information. We all know that an approaching source of sound, such as a whistle or horn blast, has a slightly higher pitch than if the source were standing still. Also that a receding source has a lower pitch. This is known as the DOPPLER shift in pitch. In 1848 the French physicist Armand Hippolyte Louis FIZEAU pointed out that a similar change in frequency could be expected to occur with light, but usually the velocity of the source is so small in comparison with the velocity of light that no obvious change in color results. However, with the spectrograph small shifts in the positions of spectral lines can be detected. Measurements of the amount of the shifts indicate the speed at which the source is moving radially along the line of sight and whether it is approaching or receding. From such Doppler FIZEAU SHIFTS astronomers can determine the radial velocity of any luminous source, whether a star, a solar PROMIN-ENCE or a galaxy.

The days are now long past when it was possible to photograph the spectra of only the brightest stars. By using special techniques and spectrographs which contain rapid Schmidt-type cameras, astronomers can now obtain spectrograms of objects far below the limits of visual observation. Nor are glass prisms the only available dispersive elements. Great use is now made of diffraction gratings, or mirrors and plates ruled over with many thousands of fine parallel lines to each inch. Whereas Fraunhofer worked with spectra only a few inches long, it is now possible to form a spec-trum of the sun which effectively runs upwards of several meters.

3. The sun

Compared with the earth, and indeed with any one of the nine planets which revolve around it, the sun is a body of immense size. While the earth has a diameter of nearly 8000 miles, that of the sun is 864,000 miles, or 108 times greater. In terms of volume this means that just over 1,000,000 globes each the size of our earth could be packed within the sun. Besides being the central and largest body in the solar system, the sun is by far the most massive – in fact, over 99·87 per cent of the mass of the solar system resides in the sun. The other 0·134 per cent is shared by its family of planets, together with their satellites and the large company of minor planets. The sun, through its gravitational attraction, dominates all the members of its widely scattered family. It retains the planets in their orbits of revolution and its great outpouring of light and heat makes life possible on the earth.

Although it is so large and so important as the central object of the solar system, the sun is but one star among millions and millions of other stars. It is also quite an average star as far as its size and luminosity are concerned. It appears large and brilliant in the sky because it is so near, at least by astronomical standards, being at a mean distance of about 93,000,000 miles (or one astronomical unit) from the earth. Owing to the eccentricity of the earth's orbit, however, the actual distance varies by nearly 3,000,000 miles; the distance is least in early January and greatest in early July. Yet so great is this distance that the sun's light, traveling at a speed of 186,283 miles a second, takes about $8\frac{1}{3}$ minutes to reach us. The next nearest star after the sun, the star Proxima Centauri, is so remote that its light spends no less than $4\frac{1}{3}$ *years* on its journey. Placed at the distance of Proxima Centauri, the sun would appear just like any other fairly bright star, just a point of light even when viewed through the most powerful telescope. Put another way, if the sun were placed at the distance of 8·7 light years, the distance of the brightest star Sirius, it would appear about equal in brightness to Polaris, the Pole Star.

The sun is, therefore, the only star which presents a disk and which can be studied at close quarters. This study began with the invention of the telescope and now involves the application of a large variety of observational techniques. It tells us, among other things, that the sun is not, as we might at first be tempted to think, a white-hot solid ball. It is, on the contrary, yellowish in color and entirely gaseous. Its material is certainly far less densely packed than that of the earth; the average density of the earth is about 5·5 times the density of water, that for the sun is only about 1·5 times. Even so, the material at and near the center of the sun, although gaseous, is extremely dense, subject as it is to tremendous pressures brought about by the weight of overlying material and to temperatures which are believed to soar to millions of degrees. Theoretical considerations suggest that the density, pressure and temperature of the sun's gaseous body all decrease from the center outwards to the surface.

At the apparent luminous surface of the sun, called the PHOTO-SPHERE or light-sphere, the temperature is about 6000° CENTI-GRADE. This highly complex region, some 50 to 100 miles deep, is what we see as the surface and sharp edge of the sun. Through it comes the band of RADIATION which constitutes the continuous background of the solar spectrum. Vested in it are the effects of selective absorption which give rise eventually to the many thousands of dark FRAUNHOFER LINES.

When examined through large telescopes used in first-class atmospheric conditions, the photosphere is seen to have a mottled appearance or granulation. Forming the granulation are innu

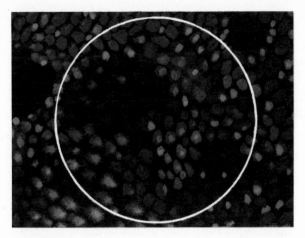

The bright granules in the sun's photosphere with the size of the earth (white circle) for comparison.

Spots on the sun.

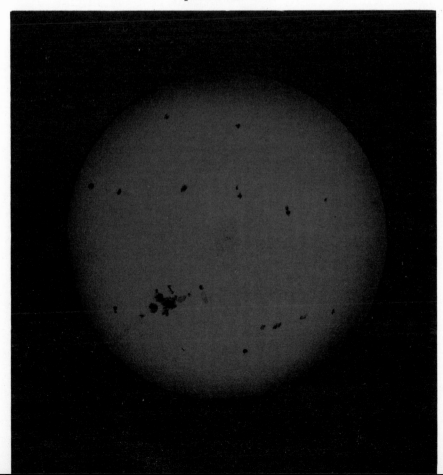

merable bright granules almost circular in shape and separated by less bright spaces. The granules, which some observers have likened in appearance to rice grains, look very small but in actuality are from 500 to 1,000 miles across. Each granule has a brief lifetime, appearing for a minute or two and then fading away to be replaced by another. They are generally considered to be the crests of ascending columns of hot gases which, on discharging their heat, move downwards and give rise to the less bright intergranular spaces.

Good visibility of the granules is confined to the central parts of the sun's face. Towards the edge or LIMB, because of the sphericity of the sun, the granules are seen at an oblique angle and therefore appear foreshortened. The photosphere appears much less brilliant near the sun's limb than at the center, for in looking towards the limb we are looking through an effectively thick layer of the solar photosphere and cannot reach very deep levels. When we look at the center of the disk, and therefore straight into the photosphere, we can see layers which are deep and bright.

From time to time, and presumably when regions of the photo-

The relative depth in the sun's atmosphere at which events can be witnessed depends on their position relative to the apparent center of the disk. The depths of penetration X and X' are the same, but involve events occurring at very different levels.

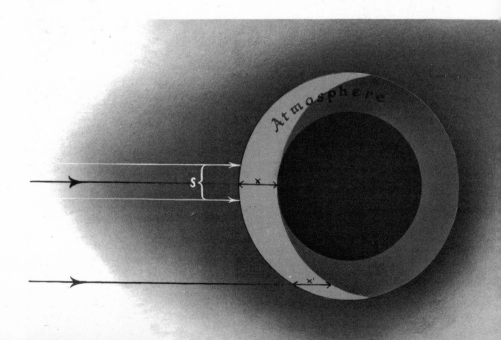

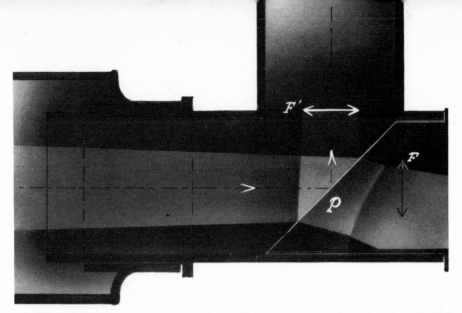

A solar eyepiece. A small part of the sunlight from an object-glass is reflected by the upper face of a thin prism (P) to form an image at F′. Most of the light and heat passes directly through the prism.

sphere become more than usually disturbed, the granules separate to leave behind them tiny dark spots called "pores". These pores can grow to form patches of considerable size known as SUN-SPOTS. Not all pores grow into spots and it may take more than one pore to form a spot or group of spots. The spots themselves appear in a large variety of shapes and sizes and can exhibit all stages of complexity. Some develop into arrays of spots so large and extensive as to cover thousands of millions of square miles. The largest spot so far recorded was that of April, 1947, which at maximum covered over 6 billion square miles or 6132 millionths of the solar hemisphere. Spots of this size, and indeed any spot upwards of 25,000 miles across can be seen with the unaided eye, but only when the sun is near the horizon or otherwise has its glare reduced by haze or fog. The fact that sunspots can be seen in this way led to their accidental discovery by the Chinese and others long before the invention of the telescope.

One of the safest and most convenient ways of observing sun-spots with a telescope is to focus the instrument so that it projects the sun's image on a white card or board. The board is placed behind the telescope at a convenient distance and the eyepiece tube is adjusted until a sharp image is formed. This is an excellent way

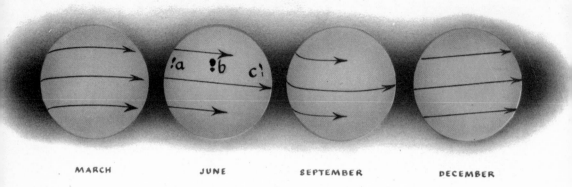

Sunspot tracks at different months

of plotting sunspots and noting their shapes and sizes. Also, it is completely safe. To hold smoked and tinted glasses between the eyepiece and the eye is to court visual disaster, for the concentration of heat in this region can be so great as to crack and splinter deep-tinted glass filters.

The telescope reveals a definite structure in sunspots. A normal spot has an almost uniform dark central region, the UMBRA, framed in a grayish surrounding, the PENUMBRA. Curiously enough, and although it appears so dark, a sunspot radiates both light and heat. The spectroscope tells us that the umbra has a temperature of about 4000° centigrade, or 2000° centigrade below that of the surrounding photosphere. At this temperature chemical compounds like titanium oxide and magnesium hydride can exist without dissociation into their constituent elements. Sunspots therefore appear dark by contrast with the hotter and brighter photosphere. Seen by themselves in isolation they would appear intensely bright. The lighter penumbra appears to be made up of highly elongated and well separated granules which have arranged themselves radially around the umbra like so many straws.

As sunspots grow and decay they are carried across the face of the sun in a general east-to-west direction by the solar rotation. The true or sidereal period of this rotation at the sun's equator is almost 25 days. The corresponding period relative to the moving earth, the synodic rotation, is 27 days. Most spots last for a few hours or days, but some of the largest and more permanent ones may exist for several months, although with considerable changes in area and form. The great spot of April, 1947, for instance, was first seen early in February and did not disappear from view until 11 May. On one occasion, in 1840–1, a spot persisted for the unusually long period of 18 months.

As a spot approaches the sun's limb it is seen more and more obliquely and appears foreshortened. This is, of course, a natural consequence of the sun's sphericity. The umbra is usually the first to disappear, and by the time the spot is almost on the limb the penumbra alone remains, appearing as a thin darkish streak. Moreover, as the spot nears the limb, the side of the penumbra nearest to the limb is the last to disappear. This effect, first noticed in detail by Alexander WILSON of Glasgow in 1774, suggests that all sunspots are depressions in the photosphere. More recent observations show that this generalization is not permissible – that in some cases the umbra is level with and even slightly above

Areas of sunspot formation. Spots in the lightly-shaded zones are comparatively rare, most spots being confined to the two darkest zones.

the photosphere. It should also be remembered that Wilson's observations were restricted to spots with circular and concentric umbrae and penumbrae, that is, to regular spots.

Another interesting feature brought about by the general east-to-west spot movement is that the sun does not rotate as a solid body but at different speeds in different solar latitudes. Within the belt most frequented by spots the rotation period increases gradually from the minimum of 25 days at the solar equator to $27\frac{1}{2}$ days at 40° north and south. These results have been confirmed by means of the spectroscope and extended to the vicinity of the poles, where the period is about $33\frac{1}{2}$ days.

Sunspots not only vary in their sizes and day-to-day numbers but also in their frequency over a long period. The fact that they vary in number over several years was first established by Heinrich SCHWABE, an amateur astronomer of Dessau in Germany. As a result of systematic observations made with small telescopes and extended over the period 1826–43, Schwabe obtained evidence of their rise and fall in number over 11 years. About 1880, Rudolf WOLF of Zürich Observatory, having collected and examined all the available sunspot observations made since the time of Galileo, found that while the length of the sunspot cycle has varied between the extremes of seven and 17 years, the mean value is 11·1 years.

Not only do sunspots increase and decrease in number and total area in a cycle of about 11 years, but the number seen at a maximum also varies considerably from one cycle to another. The lowest value for a maximum occurred in 1816, the highest in 1870 and 1947, when the numbers were three times greater than those in 1816. Sunspots also follow a definite rule or pattern in their distribution in solar latitude. This pattern was discovered in 1859 by Richard CARRINGTON, and shortly afterwards but independently by Gustav SPÖRER of Germany. The new spots at the beginning of a cycle appear in latitudes around 30° to 35° north and south. During the rise to sunspot maximum, which takes about five years, the spots tend to appear progressively in lower latitudes. This downward trend continues to the end of the cycle, by which time the spots generally occur in latitudes 5° to 10°. Yet from time to time the spots can be seen in four zones, for a few high-latitude spots of the new cycle invariably appear a year or two before the end of the old cycle.

Another prominent visual feature seen through the telescope are FACULAE, or bright streaks and patches which straggle over the sun's surface for many thousands of miles. Raised slightly above the photosphere, the faculae are best seen near the limb where they stand out in marked contrast with the darkened photosphere. They are generally, but not always, found in the vicinity of sunspots, and although regarded as mountainous upheavals of hot gas, often persist long after the associated spots have died away. Faculae are also found outside the sunspot zones, especially in the higher latitudes between 60° and 80°, but these patches are both small and short-lived.

Above the photosphere lies the immense extent of the sun's atmosphere, a region which until recent times could be observed and studied only during the brief minutes of a total solar eclipse. On these occasions the disk of the moon covers the brilliant photosphere and blots out all but the light from the atmospheric envelope. As the moon proceeds to cover more and more of the sun's face a transitory stage is reached when only the thinnest crescent of the upper parts of the photosphere is left. If the light from this thin strip is allowed to pass into a spectrograph, the resulting spectrum is that given by a glowing gas at low pressure. This gas, however, is at a temperature lower than that at the bottom of the photosphere, and its atoms selectively absorb part of the radiation which streams upwards to them. Normally this process gives rise to narrow gaps in the otherwise continuous background of the solar spectrum, the gaps are the well-known Fraunhofer lines. When seen alone, however, this gas gives a bright-line or emission spectrum, which when observed in this way is called the "FLASH SPECTRUM".

During the brief period of totality the eclipsed sun appears to be surrounded by a narrow rosy fringe which J. Norman LOCKYER in 1868 named the CHROMOSPHERE or colour sphere. This fringe is actually a layer of tenuous gas some 10,000 miles deep. At its top, where the gas density is very low, only the lighter

Prominences on the sun's limb.

gases, hydrogen, helium and ionized calcium are found. Its reddish color comes from the predominantly red light of glowing
hydrogen, or more precisely, from the bright red Hα line of its
emission spectrum.

In the chromosphere are found prominences, or enormous
bright clouds which look like flames when seen on the edge of the
sun and therefore projected against the sky. Special techniques
now enable astronomers to observe the prominences without
having to wait for a total solar eclipse. In one device, introduced
by Pierre JANSSEN and independently by Lockyer just after the
eclipse of 1868, it is possible to see the prominences as they rise
from the edge of the sun. The slit of a high dispersion spectroscope is set precisely on the edge of the sun's image formed by

a large telescope. Then, when the slit is widened to embrace the chromosphere (and only the chromosphere), the bright Hα line is seen no longer as a line but as an image of the source – the prominence itself.

With another instrument, the SPECTROHELIOGRAPH, introduced in 1891 by George HALE of Yerkes Observatory, the entire solar disk can be photographed in monochromatic light, or light of a single narrow waveband. In operation the narrow slit of a high dispersion spectrograph is allowed slowly to scan an image of the sun. Simultaneously the isolated slit image in, say, Hα light, traverses a suitably sensitized photographic plate and in so doing builds up an image of the sun in that light. The resulting SPECTROHELIOGRAMS show not only the hydrogen prominences at the limb but also those on the sun's disk; the latter appearing as dark filaments projected on the bright photosphere. By selecting other radiations like those of the H and K lines of ionized calcium in the violet, photographs of the distribution of clouds of calcium gas in the chromosphere can also be secured. By 1924, Hale had modified the spectroheliograph so that the prominences could be observed visually. In the new instrument, the SPECTRO-HELIOSCOPE, the slits oscillated to and fro so rapidly that, through persistence of vision, the observer with his eye behind the

Vortices centered over a pair of sunspots as revealed by a spectroheliogram in Hα light.

second oscillating slit saw an image of the sun in Hα light. By this
means astronomers could observe not only the forms but also the
movements of the prominences.

Similar results are now obtained by using POLARIZING MONO-
CHROMATORS based on the types devised by Bernard LYOT of
France, Yngve ÖHMAN of Sweden, and J. W. Evans of the United
States. These act as highly selective optical filters which transmit
very narrow bandwidths and enable monochromatic images of the
entire solar disk to be formed. In addition, and thanks to the
pioneer work of F. C. and R. R. McMath of the McMath-Hulbert
Observatory, motion picture techniques are now being successfully
used to record solar changes in monochromatic light.

The prominences are perhaps the most remarkable of all solar
phenomena. They appear in a great variety of forms. The most
spectacular are those of the "eruptive" type. These often take the
form of a huge arch with a span of several hundred thousand miles
which expands outwards like a gigantic spiralling smoke ring. An
impressive prominence of this type, recorded on June 4, 1946,
reached the incredible height of 1,060,000 miles, or well in excess
of the sun's diameter. In another eruptive type, bright jets or
rockets of material shoot almost vertically from the photosphere,
reach many thousand miles, and continue their looping trajector-
ies to fall back towards the sun. In comparison with these and
other highly violent types, many prominences are more or less
quiescent. These look like pyramids, loops, feathers, trees, and
clumps of trees, and have an average height of about 50,000 miles.
They may show little change over many days, or even weeks.

Not all prominences initially rise upwards from the sun. Motion
pictures of the edge of the sun in the red light of hydrogen show
that clouds of glowing gas materialize high up in the chromosphere. Material then pours downwards from the cloud in the
form of graceful streamers and jets, giving the whole the appearance of a fountain of fire. Motion pictures also make it quite clear
that, contrary to expectation and earlier ideas, the visible matter
in most prominences moves downwards to the solar surface.
According to one theory the material rises upwards in the form of
innumerable spicules or tiny prominences which become in-

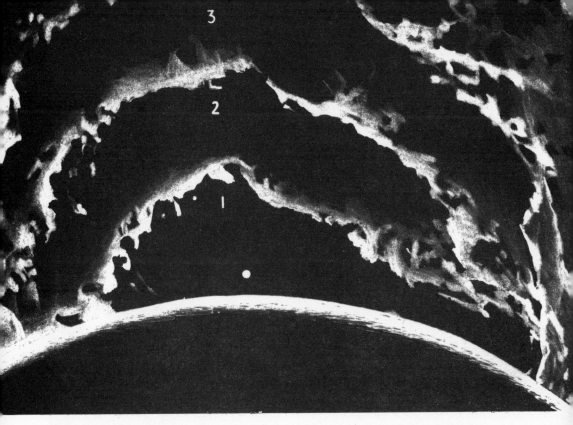

Three stages in the development of a large arched prominence. The small disk just above the sun's limb represents the earth, drawn to scale for comparison.

visible at heights above the chromosphere. The gas becomes visible again on acquiring electrons and descending into regions of higher pressure.

Prominences can be broadly classified according to their positions in solar latitude. Those which appear within the sunspot zone, that is, between latitudes 40° north and 40° south, follow sunspots closely in number and in changing position in latitude. During the years when the sunspots are numerous so also are the prominences, especially the larger and more spectacular types, although both quiescent and eruptive forms are seen in the sunspot zone. Prominences in the form of loops, inflowing streamers and surges are also closely associated with large and active sunspots and sunspot areas. Those that occur outside the sunspot zone reach their greatest frequency between sunspot minimum and maximum in about latitudes 50° north and 50° south. They then appear at increasingly higher latitudes until they are found in the polar regions just after sunspot maximum. Around sunspot minimum the prominences reappear in latitudes 50° north and south and increase in frequency as the new cycle gets under way. The majority are of the quiescent type, but some which appear to be quiescent have been known to disrupt with explosive violence.

Monochromatic studies of the sun also reveal the interesting fact that just above the sunspots the chromosphere has a vortex structure. This phenomenon was first described in 1908 by Hale, who saw the effect on spectroheliograms taken in Hα light. It occurred to him that these vortices might produce detectable MAGNETIC FIELDS in the sunspot centers, on the basis that electrons whirled round by a vortex would constitute an electric cur-

The corona, seen during a total solar eclipse, at the time of sunspot maximum.

rent which in turn would give rise to a magnetic field. The
means for testing this was readily available, for in 1896 Pieter
ZEEMAN had found that a magnetic field splits the spectral lines
emitted by atoms into component lines, whose number and separation indicate the strength and direction of the magnetic field.
Hale found not only that the spectra of sunspots show the
characteristic Zeeman effect, but also that the strengths of the
sunspot fields were surprisingly great, especially in view of the
enormous areas they covered.

Even more remarkable was the discovery by Hale that in the
case of sunspot groups which consisted of two main spots, the two
were bipolar, or of opposite magnetic polarities. For a group north
of the solar equator the leading or westerly spot had S polarity,

The corona, seen during a total solar eclipse, at the time of a sunspot minimum.

while the following spot had N polarity. For bipolar groups south of the equator the pattern of polarities was reversed. With a few exceptions this state of affairs continued until 1913, the time of the commencement of the next 11-year cycle, when the new bipolar spots were found to have interchanged their polarities. On this basis the sunspot period is actually 22 years rather than the 11 years indicated by sunspot frequencies.

Also from the vicinity of sunspots come FLARES, the most violent of solar phenomena. The largest and brightest, although the most rare, can be seen by visual means with an ordinary telescope. They then appear as white patches which rise suddenly to intense brilliance and then in a matter of minutes fade into obscurity. The first recorded observation of a flare was made on 1 September, 1859, by Carrington and Richard Hodgson. Carrington was at the time making routine sunspot observations and was quite unprepared for the two patches which flared up with great rapidity within the area of an active sunspot group. On the following day, displays of aurorae and great magnetic storms occurred, but the significance of this sequence of events was not appreciated until many years later. The introduction of techniques in monochromatic light led to a sharp increase in the numbers of flares discovered, but their study was, and indeed still is, hampered by the sudden and completely unpredictable way in which they occur. They are by no means all large objects, and the majority are far smaller than the more infrequent visual types. Some rise to maximum brightness in less than ten minutes, others may take an hour or more. As we shall see later in this chapter, most flares are important for other reasons, being responsible for displays of aurorae and disturbances in the earth's magnetic field.

The chromosphere consists not only of hydrogen gas but also of helium and calcium. Helium, in fact, was found to exist on the sun before it was discovered on the earth. During the total solar eclipse of 1868, Lockyer found a hitherto unidentified line (now designated D_3) in the flash spectrum. Helium, the name given to the gas responsible for the line, was not isolated on the earth until 27 years later. Radiation from solar helium is insufficient for satisfactory photography of the sun in the light of the D_3 line.

In the coronagraph the brilliant light from the sun's photosphere is occluded by a circular disk and total solar eclipses can be "made to order."

Hale's first achievement with the spectroheliograph was to obtain photographs of the entire solar disk in the radiation of the H and K lines of ionized calcium. They revealed a new class of phenomena – the bright calcium flocculi, so called because of their fleecy appearance. Luminous hydrogen clouds (not to be confused with prominences) and the calcium flocculi are now grouped together under the general term PLAGES. They lie in the lower chromosphere, and like the faculae (to which they appear to be related) tend to gather over sunspot groups and other disturbed areas. Even so, and unlike the faculae, they can appear on any part of the sun's disk.

Outside the chromosphere lies the corona, an extensive region whose farthest reaches can be seen only during a total solar eclipse. On these occasions the corona appears as a faint pearly-white halo whose brightness is about equal to one-half that of the full moon. Its general shape varies with the sunspot cycle. During the period of minimum sunspot activity the corona stretches out equatorially in the form of long streamers on both sides of the sun. These streamers bow inwards to give the sun great "petals" or "wings" which can often be traced to distances several times the sun's diameter. Also present at this time, and far shorter than the equatorial extensions, are tufts and brushes of light in the regions of the sun's poles. As sunspot activity increases the "petals" decrease and the polar tufts increase to give the corona at sunspot minimum a fairly uniform extent.

The Zodiacal light.

In the intervals between total solar eclipses the faint radiance of the corona is completely overpowered by the sun's intense glare. Yet even if the sun's disk is occluded by some artificial means, the scattering of light by the earth's atmosphere gives the sun a halo which is far and away brighter than the actual halo of the corona. In attempts to record the corona between eclipses, and to escape from the effects of atmospheric haze, some astronomers tried out equipment at high-altitude sites. Photographic methods showed a halo round the sun, but this was still found to be due to light scattered not only by the atmosphere but also by the optical elements in the instrument itself – by the lens apertures and scratches and dust particles on the lens surfaces.

Finally, in 1931, the French astronomer Lyot introduced the coronagraph, a telescope of special design in which instrumental scattering was almost eliminated. Incorporated in the system was a circular occluder which exactly covered the sun's disk and produced artificially the appearance of a total solar eclipse. Used on the summit of the Pic du Midi in the Pyrenees, and therefore high above the mists and haze of the lowlands, the coronagraph enabled Lyot to study the prominences both visually and photographically and to secure photographs and spectrograms of the inner regions of the corona.

Work with coronagraphs at high-altitude stations like those at Pic-du-Midi, Arosa (Switzerland), Climax (Colorado) and Sacramento Peak (New Mexico) has led to great advances in our knowledge of the chromosphere and corona. Lyot himself made an extensive study of the positions and intensities of the narrow emission lines in the spectrum of the inner corona, lines which B. Edlén has shown to be due, in the main, to highly ionized atoms of iron, nickel and calcium. These bright emission lines are seen against a faint continuous spectrum which decreases rapidly in brightness with increasing distance from the limb. The fact that the atoms are highly ionized suggests that the temperature in those tenuous regions is about $1,000,000°$ centigrade – a temperature immensely higher than that of the photosphere. The fact that a continuous spectrum is present as a background indicates that free electrons in the corona scatter the incident sunlight and move at speeds so great that the dark Fraunhofer lines are blurred out of existence. Again, if the electrons are to have these speeds, the coronal gas must have an extremely high temperature.

At increasing distances beyond the inner corona, beyond a distance, that is, of some 30,000 miles from the sun's limb, the coronal emission lines gradually fade away to leave the characteristic though extremely faint solar spectrum. The light from this "outer" corona therefore appears largely to be sunlight reflected by dust particles and fragments of a meteoric nature. This material has an extremely low distribution density, and if placed in the lower levels of the corona would quickly evaporate.

In the opposite direction, away from the sun, the dust seems to extend into space for many millions of miles, but its nature and distribution are such that it cannot rightly be regarded as part of the sun's atmosphere. In all probability the dust and meteoric fragments are responsible for the ZODIACAL LIGHT, a cone-shaped area of diffuse light which extends upwards from the place on the horizon where the sun has just set or is about to rise. So faint is the light that it can be seen only in ideal atmospheric conditions. Its longer axis, which passes through the sun, lies in or near the ecliptic. It is therefore best seen when the ecliptic is steeply inclined to the horizon such as from the tropics, or in early spring or late autumn for observers in northern latitudes. On very rare occasions the zodiacal light appears more like a band than a cone and can be traced to a considerable distance across the sky; this appearance suggests that the sun is surrounded by a deep layer of material which extends outwards beyond the orbit of the earth.

Sunspots, prominences, faculae, plages, flares, and coronal streamers are probably all related phenomena, the outward expressions of some kind of commotion far below the photosphere. In these pages we have of necessity mentioned only the more evident connections. For information about other and looser correlations the interested reader must be prepared to probe more deeply into the fascinating details of solar physics. Large solar disturbances also produce striking terrestrial effects, despite the great distance which separates the sun from the earth. Here again, and by reason of the complexity of the subject, we shall draw attention to only the most evident relationships.

Of the many attempts to correlate terrestrial effects with the 11-year sunspot cycle, comparatively few have met with any measure of success. We can immediately discount the claims of those whose wishful thinking led them to find parallels between the sun-spot cycle and records of the frequencies of earth tremors, ship-wrecks, inundations, national disasters, invasions of locusts, and outbreaks of cholera. There are, however, indications that the solar cycle is reflected in certain meteorological events, but nothing really definite is known about this. In this connection an interesting study was made some years ago by A. E. Douglass, who from measurements of the diameters of the annual rings of pine and sequoia trees in northern Arizona, found that the growth rate (and hence rainfall) had varied in cycles of about 11 years.

On the other hand, similar studies by investigators elsewhere have not so far supported Douglass' findings.

Closely connected with sunspot frequency are curves for the fluctuations of the elements of the earth's magnetic field, whose intensity increases with spot frequency. A striking connection also exists between sunspots and flares on the sun and ionospheric disturbances on the earth. These disturbances, known as magnetic storms, nearly always occur after a large and active spot has crossed the central meridian of the sun's disk. With them come interruptions in both telegraphic and radio communication, and also displays of aurorae.

Many large spots, however, have crossed the sun's central meridian without heralding a geomagnetic storm. For a storm to occur the spot must have associated flare activity: the flare or flares rather than the spot itself initiates the sequence of geophysical events. It so happens that the most intense flares tend to appear with the largest spots, yet both presumably spring from some deep-seated solar activity forever hidden from our eyes.

Considerable attention has recently been given to the nature of the agencies which give rise to the IONOSPHERE, or region in the earth's upper atmosphere in which are found various electrically conducting layers. Without these layers, long-distance radio communication on the earth would be impossible, for they reflect the radio waves which otherwise would escape into space. The electrical properties of these layers are due to the presence of free IONS and electrons formed by ultra-violet and X-RAY radiation from the sun. Now flares emit intense bursts of these short-wave radiations which travel to the earth in just over eight minutes. On reaching the earth's sunlit hemisphere the radiations are absorbed by the ionized layers in the upper atmosphere, increase their free electron density and reflective properties, and cause them to drop below their usual heights. During a solar flare the lowest layer, the intensified D-LAYER, almost completely absorbs the short radio waves which it normally transmits, and thereby gives rise to an effective radio "fadeout" which can last for several hours. Long radio waves, on the other hand, receive improved reflection at the D-layer during a flare. Unfortunately the marked increase

in signal strength is offset by the corresponding enhancement of
statics produced by lightning discharges. These changes, of
course, are restricted to the sunlit hemisphere of the earth.

A large flare also ejects a stream of particles which have velocities so great that they completely leave the sun for the distant
reaches of interplanetary space. They travel at an average speed of
about 1000 miles a second, and when the beam is intercepted by
the earth, have taken just over a day to reach our atmosphere.
They consist, in the main, of electrons and hydrogen and helium
ions. When these electrically charged particles reach the higher
atmosphere, their paths are determined in part by the earth's
magnetic field. They spiral towards the earth in the vicinity of the
magnetic poles and in so doing create high-altitude electrical
currents. These streams of particles encounter atoms of very thin
air at high altitudes. As a result of the collisions, the very thin
air glows, to produce the luminous patches, streaks, arcs and
streamers of the aurora. Large swarms of particles emitted by
large and intense flares give rise to correspondingly large electrical
currents. These in turn upset the earth's magnetic field, violently
disturb needles, and induce currents in telephone and telegraph
cables which play havoc with communication. In addition, the
auroral displays associated with them are correspondingly intense and spectacular.

Large flares and active sunspots also add considerably to the
sun's output of radio waves. It is now well established that the sun
is continuously broadcasting at certain wavelengths within the
region transmitted by the "radio window", that is, at wavelengths
between about one centimeter and 20 meters. This emission is
fairly steady when the "optical sun" is quiescent – when there is
no undue activity in the form of spots, flares and prominences.
During a large flare outburst, however, the intensity of the "solar
noise" increases many thousand times, at least for receivers used
on the sunlit hemisphere of the earth. It first commanded attention on February 27, 1942, when operators at military RADAR
stations in Great Britain reported strong interference from a
source which seemed to be in the direction of the sun. The source
kept pace with the sun, vanishing at sunset and returning at sun-

rise. On February 28, an enormous sunspot associated with great flare activity crossed the sun's central meridian. There could be no doubt that the source of the interference was not, as at first thought, a new form of enemy activity, but the sun itself.

So far we have been concerned with regions above the sun's photosphere – with features revealed by the techniques of observation. When we come to consider conditions deep in the sun's interior we must use a completely different method of investigation. A theoretical sun is first constructed. This model is given a known composition and various appropriate properties, and its "behavior" is studied as a whole or in part by applying the known laws of physics. The success of any one model will always depend on how closely it approximates to the actual sun as revealed by observation.

Theoretical models have yielded results of the highest significance, not only in solar physics but also in the far wider subject of astrophysics. They indicate that the central temperature of the sun is about 13,000,000°, a temperature at which atoms have lost all their electrons. Yet despite this enormous central temperature and its great density (about 50 times that of water), the material still behaves like a gas. They also show that a star having the sun's mass, size and luminosity must consist almost entirely of hydrogen: that hydrogen and a comparatively small amount of helium comprise over 98 per cent of the sun's mass. True, the solar spectrum reveals the presence of many other elements, but the strength of their spectral lines is brought about by the effects of favorable temperature at the sun's surface. The large amount of hydrogen gives the clue to the way the sun maintains its fantastic outpouring of energy – to the concept of the sun shining not by a burning process, nor by contracting upon itself, but by the conversion of hydrogen into helium.

This atomic conversion is effected in various stages and requires the involvement of carbon. During the process mass is converted into energy, and with such efficiency that each gram of matter destroyed releases enough energy to run a 4,000 horse-power engine for a year. By this process the sun loses over 4,000,000 tons of mass every second, yet even at this rate it could go on radiating for at least another 30,000 million years.

4. The moon and eclipses

Although the sun and full moon appear to have the same size in the sky, the sun is both immensely larger and more distant than the moon. The moon, in fact, is earth's nearest natural neighbor in space, revolving around the earth at an average distance of about 238,800 miles. Its diameter is only 2160 miles, or just over a quarter that of the earth, but as satellites go it is still one of the largest in the solar system; no other planet for its size has so large a companion.

The moon travels in a slightly elliptical path around a point some 3000 miles from the earth's center, which is the center of gravity of the earth-moon system. Its distance therefore varies between the approximate limits of 221,500 miles (at PERIGEE) and 252,700 miles (at APOGEE). Held in the gravitational field of the earth, it does not fall down from the sky because of its orbital speed perpendicular to the direction of the earth's gravitational pull. This orbital speed averages about 2300 miles an hour and carries the moon through its own diameter in just under an hour. Yet even at this speed, and as seen from the earth, the moon takes about $27\frac{1}{3}$ days to complete a sidereal period, or circuit among the stars. Its motion relative to the sun is of course compounded of its motion round the earth and that of the earth in the same direction round the sun, its path in space being always concave to the sun.

The moon has no light of its own and shines by reflecting the

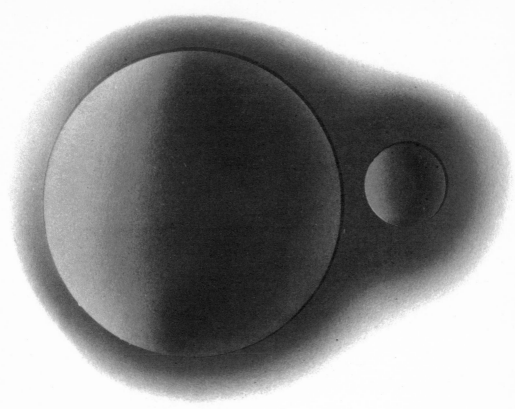

The comparative sizes of the earth (left) and moon (right).

light of the sun. We on earth see only that portion of the sunlit
hemisphere which happens to be turned towards us. For this
reason, and as the moon travels once round the earth, it goes
goes through a complete cycle of phases. The instant of new moon
occurs when the moon passes above or below the sun as seen from
the earth. Then its entire dark hemisphere faces the earth and it is
therefore invisible in the daytime sky. A day or two later, as the
moon moves away from the sun's direction, part of the sunlit
hemisphere becomes visible. This appears in the evening sky as
the familiar crescent known generally (but incorrectly) as the
"new moon". The crescent grows or waxes until the direction of
the moon makes an angle of about 90° with the direction of the
sun. One half of the sunlit hemisphere is then visible and the

The earth, moon and the distance between them to the same scale as the sun.

moon, having completed one quarter of its phase cycle, is said to be at FIRST QUARTER. As even more of the sunlit hemisphere comes into view, the phase becomes GIBBOUS and then full. At the time of full moon the entire sunlit hemisphere faces the earth; the moon is again in line with the earth and the sun, but on the side furthest from the sun. After full, and as less and less of the sunlit hemisphere becomes visible, the moon wanes through the gibbous stage to reach THIRD QUARTER, when its direction again makes about 90° with the direction of the sun. After third quarter the crescent narrows, until just a day or so before new moon it is so close to the sun that it is lost in the sun's glare.

The complete phase cycle or lunation has an average length of 29½ days. This, the synodic month, is longer than the sidereal month because it involves the earth's motion round the sun. During a month the sun appears to move forwards some 30° relative to the stars. In consequence, the moon requires about two extra days to catch up with the sun and assume the position of new moon.

As the moon revolves around the earth it also rotates on its axis, the period of axial rotation being precisely equal to the sidereal period. Because of this the moon constantly turns one and the same face towards the earth. It is possible however to see slightly more than one hemisphere owing to librations. One of these, the LIBRATION IN LATITUDE, arises because the moon's axis, although always pointing in the same direction in space, is not perpendicular to the plane of its orbit. This enables us to see slightly beyond each of its poles during a lunation. Another, the LIBRATION IN LONGITUDE, is brought about by the fact that the moon moves in an elliptical orbit. Its non-uniform speed in this orbit means that the periods of revolution and rotation are not at all times in perfect agreement – thus features a little way around the western and eastern limbs come alternately into view. Altogether the several librations enable us always to see 40 per cent of the moon's surface and as much as 60 per cent of it at one time or another.

Some idea of the nature of the remaining 40 per cent was first secured in 1959 by the Soviet space vehicle, Lunik 3. This moved in a path which enabled its two cameras, on October 7, to photo-

The earth and moon form a pair of bodies which revolve around C, the barycenter, or center of gravity of the earth-moon system.

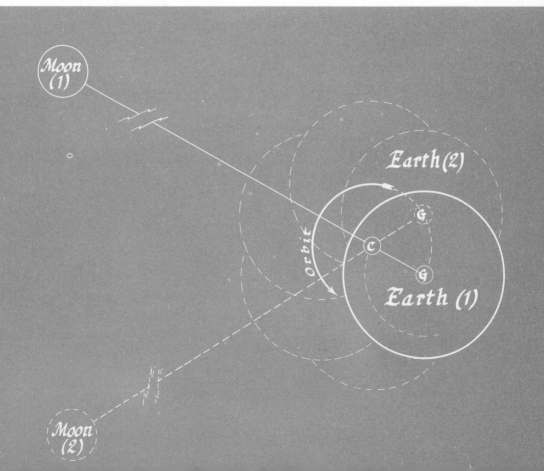

graph the far side of the moon. The pictures so secured were then radioed back to the earth on October 18, when the moon reached perigee. Photographs secured in this way show only the most prominent surface features, for the cameras must necessarily be small and picture quality is greatly reduced by the transmission process. The results so far obtained, however, show that the far side of the moon has a few small MARIA and other features similar to those observed on the near side.

The visible hemisphere of the moon can also receive sunlight by reflection from the earth. As seen in the lunar sky the earth appears about 13 times as large in area as the moon does to us and provides fully 30 times as much light. For a certain small area on the moon the earth is always overhead and merely swings slowly from side to side of its mean position owing to libration. In addition, the earth goes through a cycle of phases once a synodic month, showing at any one time always the phase opposite to that which the moon shows to us. Hence an observer stationed on the unlit part of the moon's disk just after or just before the time of the new moon would see a nearly full earth shining brightly in the lunar sky. One effect of this earthlight can be nicely observed

The total surface area of the moon (pale yellow square) superimposed on an equal-area projection of the earth.

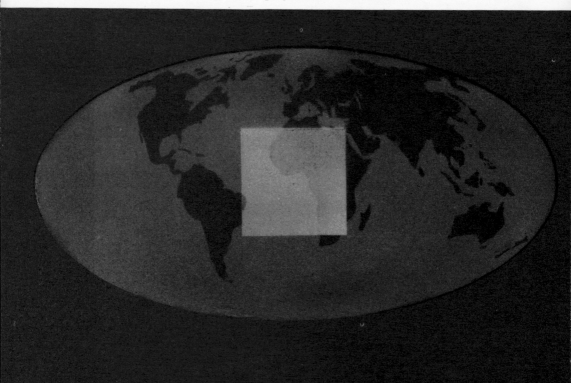

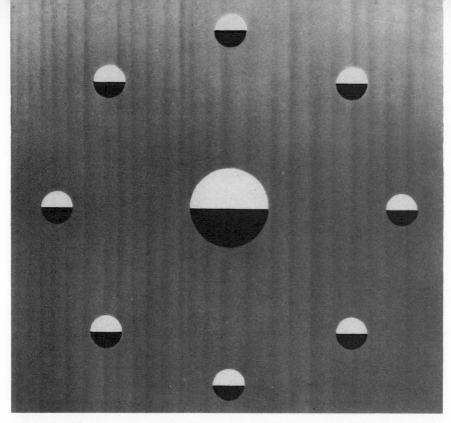

Top: The phases of the moon arise from the changing relative positions of the sun, earth and moon as the moon orbits the earth. Plan view; read anti-clockwise, starting at the top.

Bottom: The earthbound view of the moon when in the stations shown above. Read left to right, starting with the upper row.

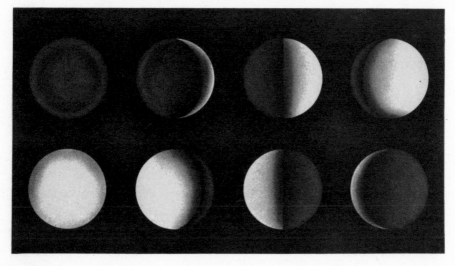

when the moon appears as a slender and therefore not too bright crescent against the darkening sky. The entire disk is then visible, the otherwise dark region shining with a faint grayish or ashen light known as the EARTHSHINE.

Although the moon can appear quite bright in the night sky, its surface reflects only 7 per cent of the sunlight it receives. Moonlight is also yellower than direct sunlight. Even at the time of full moon and with the moon high in the sky, it is difficult to read print in type of ordinary size. Nor is the illumination provided by the moon proportional to its visible sunlit area. The half moon, for example, provides only about one-tenth the illumination given by the full moon.

On the average, the moon's eastward motion among the stars causes it to rise later each day by about 50 minutes. But when this motion is combined with a northward one, that is, with increasing north declination, the moon's time of rising gets later each day by little more than 20 minutes. This situation arises around the time of the full moon nearest to the date of the autumn equinox (September 23). At this time the moon also rises almost due east at sunset. It accordingly acts as a most effective light-giver throughout several nights, and observers in mid-northern latitudes often get the impression that the moon is much brighter than at other times. This phenomenon has become known as the HARVEST MOON, and can occur in September or October. The full moon nearest to the time of the vernal equinox (March 22) also rises almost due east at sunset, but the mean interval between its times of rising on several successive nights as it moves eastward and southward can then be as large as 90 minutes a day.

The features of the "Man in the Moon" arise from the existence of bright and darker patches or MACULAE on the moon's face. Before the invention of the telescope, these patches were thought by some people to be reflections of the lands and seas of the earth. The moon, it was claimed, acted like a highly polished mirror suspended in the sky. The small telescopes used by Galileo and other astronomers of his time revealed, however, that the bright patches were full of irregularities like valleys, mountains, and curious circular formations known as craters. The darker patches

appeared comparatively smooth and were generally thought
to be seas and oceans. These appearances led Galileo and many
of his successors to make drawings and charts of the moon's
principal features, thereby laying the foundations of lunar cartography or SELENOGRAPHY. In 1647, for example, Hevelius of
Danzig produced a lunar chart which showed 250 formations
which he named. In the belief that these formations resembled
physical features on the earth, Hevelius included mountains, seas,
bays, lakes, marshes and promontories in his list of names. Then
in 1651 Giovanni Battista RICCIOLI of Bologna introduced a
completely different plan for lunar names. The craters were
named after astronomers and philosophers, while the large flat
regions were known as "Maria".

Libration. A planet moves in an orbit of eccentricity 0.4 with its period of
revolution equal to its period of axial rotation. Change in velocity with change
in angular position (shown graphically on the left) exposes alternately extra
parts of the planet's illuminated hemisphere.

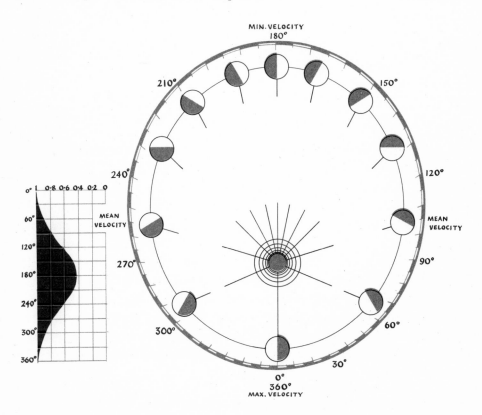

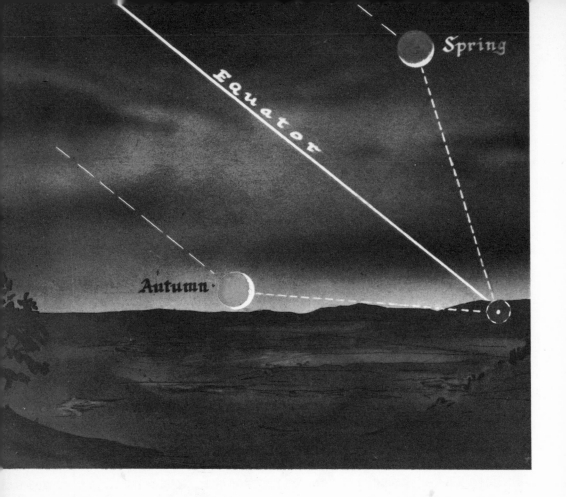

The horns of the crescent moon always point away from the sun.

From these early beginnings selenography has grown into a large and fascinating activity. Several thousand individual lunar features have been named and there seem to be no limits to the variety and profusion of the fine detail which invites study and requires incorporation into modern lunar maps. Lunar photography has of course proved invaluable in making surveys of extensive and highly complex regions, but the large photographic telescopes of professional astronomy can seldom, if ever, be spared for this work. Moreover, the finest lunar photographs taken with instruments of high resolving power fail to show all the details capable of being seen by a practised eye with a much smaller telescope. Selenography is therefore an aspect of astronomy in which amateur observers have played, and continue to play, an energetic and leading part.

Although the great lunar plains are completely devoid of water and show no signs of ever having contained water, they are still called "seas" or "maria". Individual areas bear romantic names like Mare Crisium (The Sea of Crises), Mare Humorum (The Sea of Humors), Mare Imbrium (The Sea of Showers), Mare Serenitatis (The Sea of Serenity) and Mare Tranquilitatis (The Sea of Tranquility). Several of them are roughly circular in shape. The largest, Mare Imbrium, is some 700 miles across and covers an area of about 340,000 square miles. One of the most well defined is Mare Crisium, situated near the north-western limb and visible to the unaided eye as a small dark oval spot. Although it appears oval because of foreshortening, the area is in fact almost circular

The earth and the moon appearing as crescents from a viewpoint out in space.

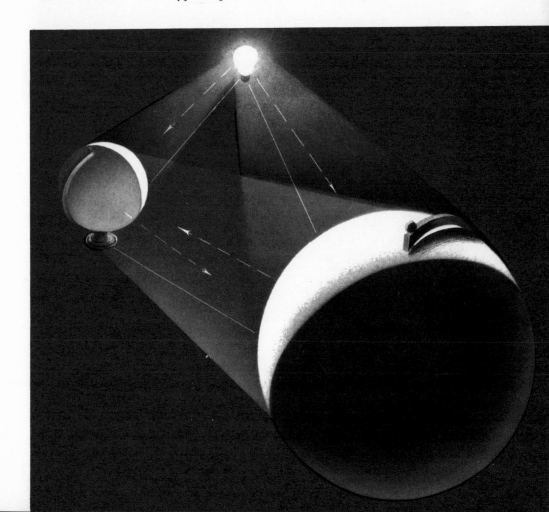

Many of the main features of the moon's surface can be seen
with just a small telescope.

and appears the more prominent because it is entirely surrounded by bright mountainous country. Mare Humorum in the south eastern quadrant also has defined boundaries, but in the north joins with Mare Nubium, which in turn runs into Oceanus Procellarum and Mare Imbrium.

Aside from the vast plains, the most striking lunar features are the RING MOUNTAINS or craters. These vary greatly in size, and somewhat in structure, from small pits and cones a few hundred yards across to great walled plains 60 to 150 miles in diameter. Small craters or CRATERLETS exist in thousands, and can be found scattered on the maria and bright areas alike. The name "crater" is now usually given to ring mountains about 3 to 30 miles across, many of which contain central mountain peaks. Next in increasing size are the RINGED PLAINS. Their massive ramparts form a circular mountain wall some 30 to 60 miles in diameter, which often rises to heights of 1 to 2 miles above the floor of the interior. Many of them, like those named after Copernicus, Theophilus, Bullialdus and Tycho, have a group of mountain peaks at or near the center of the floor, and ramparts whose inner slopes rise in a series of almost concentric

A telescopic view of Messier and Pickering,
two small craters with bright interiors.

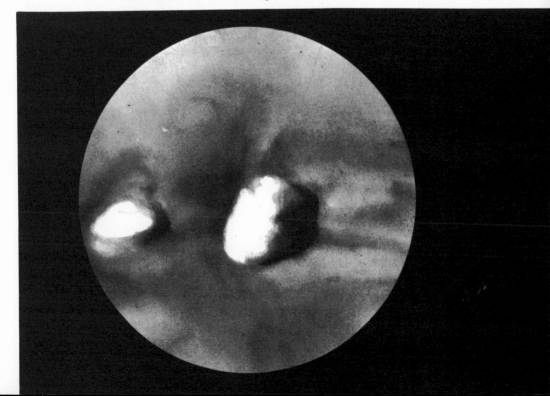

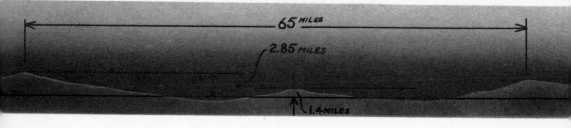

A cross-section through the ringed plain Theophilus, showing that it is a comparatively shallow or saucer-like depression.

terraces. Even larger are the walled plains, with their floors usually broken up by ridges, clefts, mountain masses, craters and crater-like depressions. Clavius, the largest of these, is about 150 miles across and contains on its floor no less than five large craters and numerous craterlets, craterpits and hills.

The most striking views of lunar formations are obtained near the TERMINATOR, or boundary between the sunlit and dark sides. This boundary, made irregular by the ruggedness of the moon's surface, sweeps twice across the disk during a lunation, traveling from west to east when the phase is waxing and from west to east when it is waning. In the first instance an object at the terminator is illumined by the first rays of the rising sun, in the second it receives the last rays of the setting sun. In both instances a lofty mountain peak or the crest of a crater wall is visible when the regions below it are shrouded in darkness. In the light of, say, a rising sun, the outer western slopes of a walled plain are seen in full relief. As the sun climbs the lunar sky its light catches the peaks of any central mountains and the more remote inner terraces. Once the floor receives its morning light, and especially if the surface is fairly smooth, objects on it cast long tapering shadows. The shadows gradually decrease in length, vanish when the sun is overhead, and then reappear as it moves down to the lunar horizon. Under a high sun most formations show but little detail, and for this reason the general telescopic view of the full moon is apt to be disappointing. A low sun, on the other hand, gives a false impression of the depths of craters and crater-like objects. They appear to be deep, pit-like excavations whereas in section they are quite shallow and saucer-like. The walls of Copernicus, for example, rise to an average height of 12,000 feet above the floor, but this is only about a twenty-sixth of the diameter of the ringed plain itself. An observer, standing in the middle of the floor of a large walled plain, would not necessarily see its distant walls since the curvature of the moon's surface might well bring them below the skyline.

When one of the maria is crossed by the terminator, careful scrutiny shows that its surface is far from smooth. Nearly horizontal illumination reveals serpentine ridges which sometimes run for hundreds of miles and with their arms, branches and associated hollows ramify and wrinkle large areas. Other regions are scarred by hillocks, isolated peaks, craters and craterlets. For any one angle of illumination the highest lunar feature casts the longest shadow. Knowing the moon's distance and the position of the sun in the lunar sky, and by measuring the angular length of a shadow, selenographers can by calculation determine the height of the object forming the shadow.

Oblique illumination is also desirable (but not always necessary) for the study and drawing of narrow sharply defined clefts, about 2,000 of which have been discovered on the moon. These are deep cracks or fissures in the surface which can often be traced for scores of miles. In some regions they form a network; the most remarkable is that near the crater Triesnecker which connects with a chain of craterlets known as the Hyginus Cleft. Also appearing as a dark line under oblique illumination just after first quarter is the remarkable "Straight Wall" on the western side of Mare Nubium. This is no wall in the accepted sense, but a straight rock face or cliff some 60 miles long which rises to a height of about 800 feet above the plain on its eastern side. The wall is clearly the result of a fault produced by a "moonquake" long ago.

Highly conspicuous features on the face of the full moon are the systems of bright streaks or rays. They are in the main associated with crater rings and craters, and in many cases radiate outwards from these objects to great distances. Through a low-power telescope the streaks appear to be fairly continuous, but a closer examination with larger instruments reveals that each long streak is made up of a number of irregular patches whose brightness seems to depend on the background. In mountainous country they are quite brilliant; on the maria they are decidedly fainter. They stretch across mountains, valleys, craters and maria without apparent interruption, have indefinite boundaries, and cast no shadows. They are permanent but are seen only at and near the time of full moon. The most splendid ray system is the one centered on Tycho, some of whose rays can be traced across nearly the entire face of the moon. Prominent systems are associated with the craters Copernicus, Kepler and Aristarchus (the most brilliant object on the moon), and there are several hundred smaller ray formations.

The nature and origin of the rays are not known, but according to one theory they are superficial markings produced as a result of meteoric impact. On the assumption that Tycho, for example, was formed by the sudden halting of a METEORITE, the resulting explosion would scatter pulverized material over a large area and show as the bright rays. Another explanation is that they are due to volcanic ash and dust ejected at the time when the central crater was active. Yet another is that deep-seated forces having Tycho as focus caused radiating cracks in the surface from which issued whitish material in the form of vapor or perhaps liquid lava. The problem appears to be one which will be solved only when man can actually stand on the ground covered by a streak and make direct physical study of the surface deposits.

The lunar craters bear no marked resemblance in either size or structure to volcanoes on the earth. Yet the fact that the force of gravity on the moon is only one-sixth of that on the earth has done much to encourage the volcanic theory of the origin of lunar craters. This theory was ably described in 1874 by the two English astronomers, James NASMYTH and James CARPENTER. Supposedly a central volcano vent threw up a fountain of ashes and stones. This material, projected to a considerable distance, accumulated to form a rampart surrounding the vent. At a later stage, when the eruptive force was sufficient only to lift the debris just clear of the vent, the material built up a cone-shaped central mountain. In some cases molten rock or lava poured from the vent or from fissures in its vicinity, thereby flooding the crater floor and even at times smoothing out the central cone.

Although features like crater terraces and flooded ring forma-tions with elevated floor levels appear to be accounted for by the theory, it has several serious drawbacks. It is difficult to conceive that in the case of Clavius, for instance, the volcanic fountain had such force as to throw debris to a distance of over 70 miles. The largest explosive craters on the earth are only about two miles across, which is physically equivalent to lunar craters 12 miles in diameter (i.e. the same force of explosion on the moon would produce a crater 12 miles in diameter). Again, many lunar craters show no traces of lava flooding and yet possess no central peak, while in others the level of the floor is *below* the general level of the surrounding regions.

Another theory, originally put forward a century ago by the German astronomer Franz von GRUITHUISEN, interprets the craters as the result of meteoric impact. It assumes that in the remote past metallic bodies from interplanetary space crashed down in large numbers on the moon's surface. The enormous energy released at each impact produced depressions immensely greater in volume and diameter than those of the meteorite itself. Debris, including powdered rock, was scattered in all directions, with the powder forming the bright ray systems found round some craters. The impact of large meteorites is also supposed to have formed circular maria like Mare Imbrium, Mare Crisium and Mare Humorum. The American astronomer Ralph B. Baldwin, who ably states the case for the meteoric theory in his book *The Face of the Moon* (1949), is among those who suggest that the depression Mare Imbrium was caused by a nickel-iron meteorite about 10 miles in diameter. After penetrating to a short distance below the surface the meteorite exploded with tremendous vio-lence to form an immense crater about 350 miles across and six or seven miles deep. Great low-flying masses fanned outwards to smash long furrows or valleys through the surrounding high-lands, thereby forming, among others, the magnificent "Alpine Valley". Later the crater filled with lava which in some parts spilled over to flood other regions and produce maria far distant from the erupting sources.

If meteorites at some remote time in the past had bombarded the moon they would most certainly have given the earth a similar treatment. Yet compared with the lunar craters those now visible on the earth are insignificant in both size and number. The almost circular Barringer Crater in Arizona is definitely meteoric in origin and is perhaps the best preserved of all the terrestrial craters. Its diameter is only about 4150 feet and the rim rises to no more than 150 feet above the surrounding plain. The largest terrestrial meteor crater so far discovered is near Lake Ungava in northern Quebec, and is about two miles across. Numerous craters far larger than these may perhaps have been obliterated by disruptive forces operative over EONS of geological time.

If the craters on the moon were formed by meteoric impacts, they should be distributed at random over the lunar surface. A study of the locations of craters and walled plains, however, shows that they tend to be aligned in chains, clusters and pairs. Furthermore, when one formation (as is often the case) breaks into its neighbor, the overlapping crater is invariably the smaller of the two. One naturally assumes that the overlapping crater is the younger formation, but in the terms of the meteoric theory this means that the largest meteorites fell first – a conclusion which, to say the least, seems to be highly improbable.

The fact that many craters form chains suggests that they are arranged along lines of crustal weakness. This notion brings us back again to a volcanic viewpoint, and in particular, to the interesting theory of "LUNAR DOMES" proposed in 1927 by the English astronomer, H. G. Tomkins. According to this, gas and molten lava from the moon's interior pushed up the semi-solid surface layers to form a LACCOLITH or domed swelling like a blister. As more and more material forced itself into the dome, the surface "skin" fissured and collapsed into a lake of lava which, on subsiding and cooling, left a circular walled plain complete with central peak and floor details like ridges and craterlets.

Many selenographers now favor theories which involve both

The track of the moon's shadow over the earth's surface.

meteoric and volcanic considerations. It is certain that titanic forces at periods in the remote past moulded and chiseled the moon's features into the forms that we see today – into forms which have survived the passage of millions of years without undergoing any major changes. There are reasons for supposing that this state of affairs will continue for millions of years to come, the more so because the moon has no perceptible atmosphere. The remarkable but grim landscape, spread out beneath a scorching sun, is clearly both airless (or nearly so) and waterless. There are no clouds, seas, rivers or lakes; there can be no wearing away of the rocks by erosion or winds. If the moon had at one time an atmosphere, it long ago escaped into space. The jagged mountain peaks, rising in some instances to heights which surpass the height of Mount Everest, are unsmoothed by the action of frost, wind and rain. No half-lights soften the harshness of the rocky and rugged wilderness; each and every shadow is of exquisite sharpness. Far from being a source of moisture and a promoter of fertility as the ancients believed it to be, the moon is a silent barren world in such immediate contact with the vacuum of space as to be completely hostile to life as we know it.

In the absence of an appreciable atmosphere, the lunar sky has a background of the deepest black. Against this the Milky Way and myriads of stars shine out with exceptional brilliancy. Dominating it all is the dazzling glare of the sun and the softer light of the earth with its changing phases. Occasionally the earth covers the sun to bring about a total solar eclipse. At these times the dark disk of the earth is surrounded by a bright halo of reddish light, affording at once a spectacle of incredible beauty and evidence of the filtering action of the earth's atmosphere.

During the lunar day, and when the sun is high in the sky, the rocky surface attains a temperature above that of boiling water. Yet during the lunar night this surface heat leaks into space so effectively that the temperature falls almost to that of liquid air. Not all the heat, however, is radiated away, and because of this the moon is a source of continuous but very weak radio emission. While one part of this emission is reflected solar energy, the other comes from the moon's own store of thermal energy. Some of the sun's heat flows by conduction below the moon's surface and remains in deeper regions during the lunar night. That the conduction of heat in this case is a slow process is indicated by the fact that the thermal radiation of wavelength 1·25 centimeters does not reach its maximum intensity until nearly four days after the time of full moon. The moon's surface may in some regions be dust several miles deep. The dust, it is suggested, was formed (and is being formed) by the action of ultra-violet and X-ray radiation on the surface layers of exposed rocks. This "weathering" process has been in progress over an immense period of time, as also have been the impacts of small meteorites. Millions of meteorites daily dash into the earth's upper atmosphere, but by friction with the air they are vaporized. They end their lives in brief trails of light at heights of between 50 to 150 miles above the ground. If the moon has no atmosphere whatever, these bodies, ranging in size from tiny grains to fragments several feet across, would crash into the surface, thereby adding still further to the production and accumulation of lunar dust.

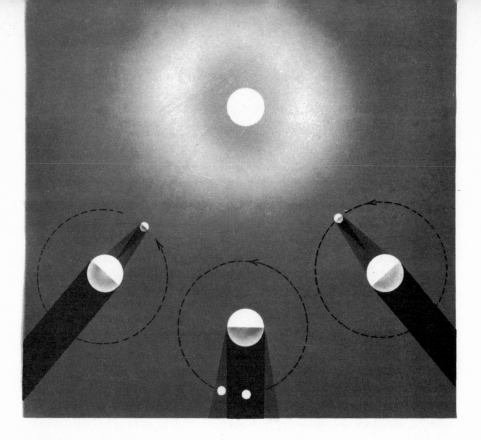

Reasons for different types of eclipse. *Left:* total eclipse of the sun. *Center:* penumbral and total phases of lunar eclipse. *Right:* annular eclipse of the sun.

Does the static appearance of the lunar landscape mean that no visible change whatever can take place on the moon? Many selenographers have thought otherwise, and in support of their contention have drawn attention to apparent changes in the form, coloration and visibility of certain areas. Among the oddities reported are snow, ice crystals, hoar-frost, dark areas of vegetation, active volcanoes and even shadowy masses of moving insects. Every change in lighting and the consequent shift of light and shadow cause quite marked changes in the aspect of many formations. Small wonder therefore that even experienced observers have been deceived. In 1954, for example, some observers thought that they could see a great natural bridge near the eastern boundary of Mare Crisium. The "discovery" was given considerable publicity, and unfortunately so, for it has since been shown that the "bridge" was nothing more than a curious lighting effect. More recently, on the morning of November 4, 1958, the Soviet astronomer Nikolai A. KOZYREV noticed that the outlines of the central mountain mass of the walled plain Alphonsus had become blurred by a reddish haze. It so happened that he had secured a spectrogram of this region just before the time of the visual observation. The spectrogram showed emission bands of diatomic carbon in the region of the red patch, but these were absent on a spectrogram taken immediately afterwards. While it is possible that Kozyrev witnessed a glowing gas cloud, the product of volcanic activity, it is significant that a most careful scrutiny of the region made later by Gerard P. KUIPER with an 82-inch reflector of the McDonald Observatory, Texas, failed to reveal any changes at all.

As the earth and the moon travel around the sun they are each accompanied by a long tapering shadow whose tip or apex is always directed away from the sun. The lengths of the shadows depend on the distances of the earth and the moon from the sun and also on their actual sizes. At its mean distance of about 93,000,000 miles from the sun, the earth casts a shadow 859,000 miles long. The shadow therefore extends far beyond the orbit of the moon, and at the moon's distance has a breadth of about $2\frac{2}{3}$ times the diameter of the moon. The length of the moon's shadow averages 232,100 miles, which means that on the average its apex falls short of the earth by 6,800 miles.

Eclipses of the sun occur when the moon passes directly between the sun and the earth. Their appearance depends on the length of the moon's shadow and the position of the observer relative to the shadow. For a total eclipse of the sun, for example, the moon's shadow must reach at least to the earth's surface, and the observer must be in the area of the shadow formed on that surface. Only in these circumstances will the moon appear to have the same apparent size as the sun and also be so placed as to cover completely the dazzling photosphere. If the observer happens to be just outside the shadow area, he sees a partial eclipse. The moon then partially covers the disk of the sun, and the

amount of uncovered sun increases as the observer moves farther
and farther away from the shadow area.

The width of the shadow area averages only 60 to 70 miles and
cannot exceed more than about 170 miles when the sun is more or
less overhead. It is also a moving area for, owing to the motion of
the moon, the apex of its shadow moves in space at the rate of
about 2,100 miles an hour. When it strikes the earth perpendicu-
larly, and because it moves in the same direction as that in which
the earth is rotating, its speed relative to an observer is less than
its speed in space. For an observer in latitude 45° north or south,
the shadow area moves at about 1360 miles an hour and in so
doing describes a narrow path, generally called the "track" or
"shadow" of the eclipse, over the earth's surface. Astronomers
wishing to observe a particular total solar eclipse can predict the
location and extent of the track and hence can decide well in advance where to set up their instruments. They often travel great
distances for this purpose, but having done so must be content
with a few minutes' observing time, and then only if the sky is
clear. Even under the most favorable conditions, with the observer on the earth's equator and the eclipse occurring at noon, the
duration of totality can never exceed 7 minutes 40 seconds.

When, owing to the moon's increased distance, the apex of the
moon's shadow fails to reach the earth, the observer in line with it
and the sun sees an ANNULAR ECLIPSE. The moon then looks smaller
than the sun, and on passing in front of the sun, covers all but a thin
uniform ring or annulus of the photosphere. Eclipses of this kind
are of little scientific interest, for the annulus is sufficiently bright
to overpower completely the faint light of the chromosphere and
corona. Here again, if the observer leaves the central line of the
eclipse track, the eclipse will be seen as only a partial one.

Solar eclipses are restricted not only to certain places on the
earth's surface for any one eclipse but also to certain times. They
are fairly numerous; from two to five occur each year, but
from a given location a total solar eclipse can be seen, on the
average, only once in 360 years. If the moon moved exactly along
the ecliptic, there would be a solar eclipse at the time of every new
moon. The plane of the moon's orbit, however, is inclined at an

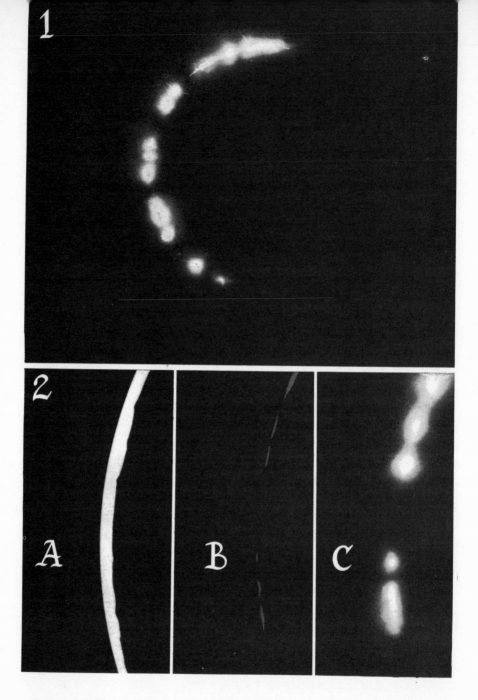

1. Baily's Beads. 2a. The irregular limb of the moon seen near the sharp edge of the sun. b. At totality small portions of the sun's edge shine through the lunar valleys. c. Irradiation of the brilliant portions gives them a bead-like appearance.

angle of nearly 5° 9′ to the ecliptic. Because of this the moon at the time of new moon normally passes a little above or below the sun, so that its shadow misses the earth and no eclipse takes place. Half of the moon's path therefore lies north of the ecliptic, while the other half lies south of it. The two crossing points are known as the NODES, and eclipses always take place when the moon is at or within a certain distance (known as the eclipse limit) from the nodes.

A total eclipse of the sun is one of nature's most impressive spectacles. As the moon creeps over the sun's disk the landscape assumes an unnatural appearance under the fading and lurid light. Tiny patches of light on the ground under trees, instead of being circular blurs, become little crescents, each an exact counterpart of the shape of the disappearing sun. Animals, especially birds, quickly sense that something unusual is afoot, for the deepening gloom is altogether different in its onset and character from that of sunset. Then comes the eastwards onrush of the moon's shadow area, and as the last slip of direct sunlight disappears the stars shine out in the darkened sky. For a few minutes all animate nature is hushed, to stir again as the stars vanish with the first rays of the emerging sun.

Since the edge of the moon is rough and irregular, the last thread of the sun's crescent breaks up into a number of rounded and oblong patches and looks like a string of bright beads. This phenomenon, known as BAILY'S BEADS, was first described in detail by Francis Baily during an annular eclipse in 1836. During totality the shining chromosphere gives the moon a bright rosy rim, and from its edge rise solar prominences which early observers mistook for red flames. Also around the moon extend the pearly-white brushes and streamers of the corona. Before 1931, when Lyot introduced the coronagraph, the corona could be studied only during the relatively few times of a total solar eclipse.

Total eclipses of the sun provided opportunities for testing an important consequence of Albert EINSTEIN's General Theory of Relativity. According to the theory, formulated in 1915, light is deflected from its otherwise straight-line path when it traverses a gravitational field. The deflection of starlight which passes close to the sun should therefore cause the stars which form the background for the sun to appear displaced from their normal positions. If these stars are photographed during a total solar eclipse and then at some later date when the sun is in another part of the sky, a comparison of the two plates should reveal small but measurable displacements of the star images away from the eclipsed sun. Evidence for this EINSTEIN EFFECT, as it is called, was first obtained during the eclipse of 1919. Further data, obtained during the eclipse of 1922 and involving measured angular displacements of only 1·72 seconds of arc for a star at the sun's limb, agreed closely with the results predicted by theory.

Eclipses of the moon occur when the earth's shadow falls on the moon. For this to happen the moon must be full and also at or within a certain distance from the nodes. Only then will the sun, earth and moon be arranged in this order and in approximately the same straight line.

As the earth's shadow moves over the face of the moon its edge is seen to be circular. This feature, coupled with the size of the

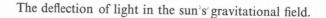

The deflection of light in the sun's gravitational field.

Sun

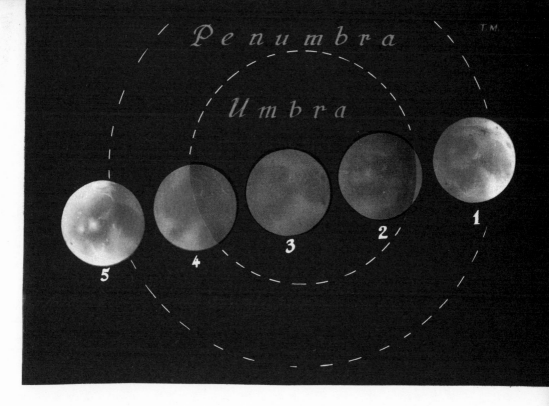

The progressive change in the moon's appearance as it passes through the penumbra and umbra of the earth's shadow. 1 and 5, partial eclipse in the penumbra, 2 and 4, partial eclipse, 3, total eclipse.

shadow at the moon's distance, was used to advantage by early astronomers. Aristotle, for instance, deduced from the earth's circular shadow on the moon at eclipse that the earth is a sphere. Aristarchus in the third century B.C. compared it with the apparent radius of the moon and thereby attempted to determine the moon's distance. By using this method, Hipparchus estimated that the distance of the moon is about 59 times the radius of the earth, a remarkably good result.

The time from the moon's entrance into the shadow of the earth to its emergence is usually about two hours. For about half this time the moon is totally eclipsed, but not in the sense that it is completely dark. Instead, its form can usually still be seen, shining with a dull reddish-brown light of hue and intensity which vary from eclipse to eclipse. This light is due to the optical properties of the earth's atmosphere. In passing through this atmosphere

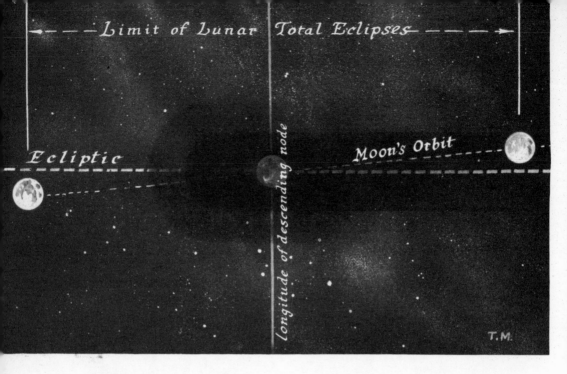

Eclipses of the moon can only occur within certain limits centered on the nodes; at other times the moon lies outside the band along the ecliptic which defines the breadth of the earth's shadow at the moon's distance.

sunlight is both refracted into the moon's geometrical shadow and scattered so that only the longer wavelengths get through. During the eclipse the temperature of the moon's surface falls in about an hour from its high midday value almost to that of a lunar night. This rapid change, operating over long periods of time, has probably been an important agent in producing the gradual exfoliation or surface disintegration of the lunar rocks.

A study of the eclipse limits for the sun and moon shows that there must be at least two eclipses a year, both of which will be solar. It is not possible to have more than seven eclipses within a year; of these at least two or as many as five will be solar. Lunar eclipses are rarer than solar; in some years none occur and the maximum number possible is only three. When there are seven eclipses in a year, five are solar and two lunar, or four solar and three lunar.

Eclipses run in cycles in that they are repeated in very nearly the same order after the SAROS period of 18 years 11 days. This period contains 223 lunations and in it the sun makes 19 returns and the moon 242 returns to the same node. Hence at the end of a Saros, the sun, moon and node return almost to the same positions as before. Operative in this repetition is the retrograde motion of the nodes. They are by no means fixed points on the ecliptic but regress slowly relative to the fixed stars to make one complete revolution in approximately $18\frac{2}{3}$ years. In other words, the plane of the moon's orbit is not fixed in space but rotates in relation to the plane of the earth's orbit around the sun.

For the precise prediction of the times of eclipses the moon's motion must be determined with considerable accuracy. This is no easy matter, for the motion of the moon is extremely complex. One peculiarity of the motion, very small in amount, is that known as the SECULAR ACCELERATION of the moon. A comparison of ancient with modern eclipses reveals that the moon's speed in its orbit is increasing, but so slowly that in order to measure the

Total eclipse of the sun by the earth, seen from a point in space, showing coronal trace and zodiacal light.

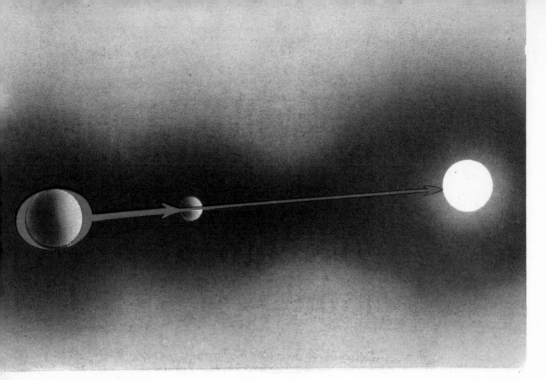

When the sun, moon and earth are in line with each other, solar and lunar tides combine to give a Spring Tide, or maximum daily range in the height of the tide.

rate of increase observations extending over many centuries are necessary. This slow acceleration of the moon means also that the moon is getting farther away from the earth at the rate of about five feet a century while the lunar month is growing longer and longer. At the present rate the average distance of the moon will have increased by about 5,000 miles in the next 586,000,000 years. In the far distant future, therefore, the moon will always appear smaller than the sun and total solar eclipses will be impossible.

The secular acceleration of the moon is a result of tidal friction. The attraction of the moon (and of the sun to a lesser degree) raises tides in both the body of the earth and in the waters which cover its surface. As a result the earth is distorted, but in such a way that the axis of its elongation lies in the direction of the moon. That it can be slightly distorted in this way shows that it is not absolutely rigid but possesses an inherent elasticity coupled with an average rigidity which is about twice that of steel. There is also a double uplifting of the surfaces of the seas and oceans at opposite sides of the earth. Although these heaped-up waters tend to re-

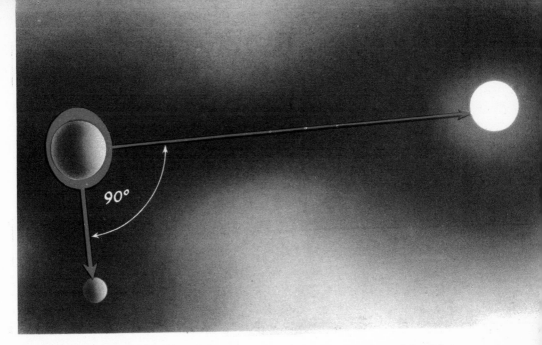

The height of the tides raised by the moon alone is about twice that of the tides raised by the sun alone. When the moon is 90° away from the sun the effects work against each other to give a Neap Tide, or minimum daily range in the height of the tide.

main under the moon, they are carried forward by the earth's rotation and hence are always slightly ahead of the moon. They therefore exert a small forwards pull on the moon and hasten it on its monthly path round the earth.

The tidal bulges also act as a kind of brake and slow down the earth's rotation; calculations based on eclipse data suggest that the day is lengthening at the rate of nearly one thousandth of a second a century. Long ago the earth raised great tides on the smaller molten moon and slowed down its rotation to such an extent that it now presents one and the same face always towards the earth. The moon continues to give similar treatment to the earth and eventually the earth will turn one and the same face to the moon. It has been estimated that this will take place after the next 50 billion years; the day will then equal the month in length, each being equal to about 47 of our present days. If this state is reached, the moon will then slowly spiral inwards towards the earth. After many more thousands of millions of years it may well come near enough to be torn to pieces by tidal forces.

5. The planets

While the earth's gravitational force reaches to the moon, it does not end there but extends to the remotest regions of interstellar space. The same is true of every other body in the universe and certainly of the sun, despite the fact that the planetary system extends only to Pluto, the most distant of the planets. Yet the system the sun controls so effectively is a magnificent one, containing as it does nine major planets and vast numbers of smaller bodies which include minor planets, comets and meteorites.

Compared with the earth, the major planets are large globes, but all of them are dwarfed by the sun. They are also separated from the sun and from each other by distances that are enormous in comparison with their sizes. To obtain some idea of these distances, imagine that the sun is represented by a globe 2 feet in diameter. On this scale the earth will be no larger than a pea at a distance of just over 200 feet, and Pluto can be represented by a pin's head at a distance of two miles. In this model Jupiter, the largest of the planets, will be about the size of an orange and will require an orbit nearly a quarter of a mile in diameter. The nearest star will then be 10,000 miles away.

The major planets move round the sun in nearly circular orbits and in the same direction. The planes of their orbits are but slightly inclined to that of the earth, so that as seen from the earth the planets are always within the band or belt of the zodiac.

Two of the planets, Mercury and Venus, are called "inferior planets" but only in the sense that they move in paths which lie within the earth's path round the sun. For this reason, and as seen from the moving earth, their angular distances from the sun, or ELONGATIONS, cannot exceed certain values. Mercury, for example, has an average maximum elongation of only 25° which it attains either on the eastern or the western side of the sun. When on the eastern side, Mercury sets after the sun and appears as an evening star. On these occasions, and from the middle latitudes, the planet is never seen for more than two hours after sunset or for more than two hours before sunrise. It is therefore rather elusive and is seldom seen by a casual observer. On the most favorable occasions, however, and when the air is very clear, Mercury can rival Sirius and almost equal Jupiter in brightness.

Like the Greek messenger-god of that name, Mercury is small and swift. Its diameter, 3,100 miles, makes it the smallest planet;

The orbits of the planets out to Jupiter drawn to scale. The double line between Mars and Jupiter indicated the "mean orbit" of the asteroids.

☿ Mercury, ♀ Venus, ⊕ Earth, ♂ Mars, ♃ Jupiter.

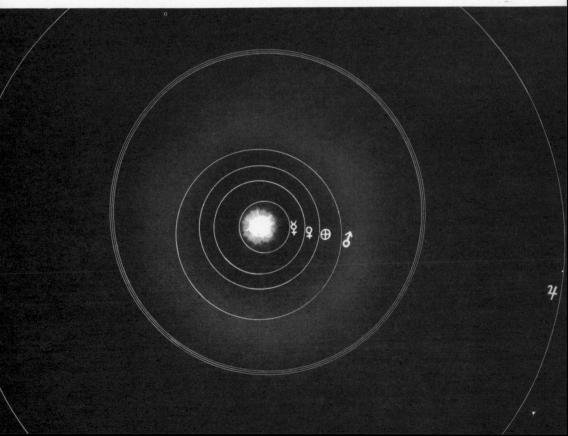

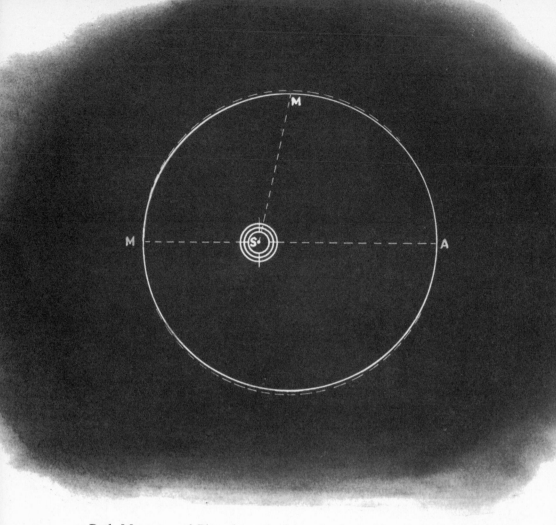

Both Mercury and Pluto have the least circular orbits of all the planets. The orbit of Mercury (solid line) is compared with an eccentric circle (dotted line).

as many as seven globes each the size of Mercury could be packed inside the earth. Being close to the sun it revolves around the sun with a mean period of only 88 days and travels at a speed within the range of 23 to 35 miles a second. Its mean distance from the sun is 36,000,000 miles, but owing to the comparatively high eccentricity of its orbit (0·206), its distance varies from 28,600,000 miles to 43,400,000 miles.

As seen from the earth, Mercury appears to swing from side to side of the sun. When nearest to the earth and therefore between the earth and the sun, it is said to be at INFERIOR CONJUNCTION.

If at that time it is at or near a node, and therefore in direct line with the sun and the earth, it appears as a small black dot that moves across or transits the sun. These transits occur only occasionally and when they do they occur within a few days of May 7 or November 9. From inferior conjunction the planet moves towards and past its maximum eastern elongation, and after about 58 days is again in approximate line with the sun and the earth or at SUPERIOR CONJUNCTION on the far side of the sun. It then moves through maximum western elongation to complete the return to inferior conjunction in an average SYNODIC PERIOD of 116 days. During this period, and because we see its sunlit hemisphere from all angles, the planet also goes through a cycle of phases, changing greatly in both brightness and apparent size. The phases cannot be seen without the aid of a good telescope.

An interesting feature connected with Mercury is that the major axis of its elliptical orbit rotates round the sun at the rate of 45 seconds of arc a century. This long axis is known as the line of APSIDES; when a planet is at one end of this line and nearest to the sun it is at PERIHELION; when it is at the other end and furthest from the sun, it is at APHELION. According to Einstein's

Left: the apparent size of the sun as seen from various points in Mercury's orbit, compared with the sun seen from the earth. *Right:* the amount of solar radiation per unit area, at the same points, compared with the earth (1, 2 and 3 correspond with maximum, mean and minimum distance from the sun).

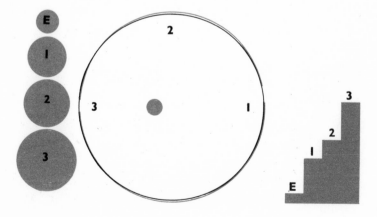

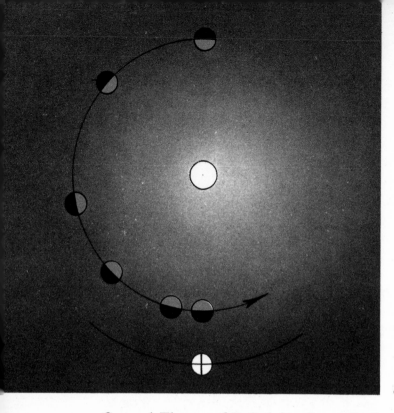

Since the orbit of Venus lies within that of the earth there is great variability in the distance between the two planets as well as a complete range of phases.

General Theory of Relativity the perihelion for any planet must advance slowly in the same direction as the planet moves. The perihelion movement can be detected only in the case of Mercury, for which the observed rate is almost in exact agreement with that predicted by theory.

Mercury appears to have a solid surface, but because its mass is so small (probably only about an eighteenth that of the earth) it has retained no perceptible atmosphere. Dusky markings seen on its disk have every appearance of being permanent features. They reveal that the planet keeps virtually the same face towards the sun – that it rotates once on its axis for one revolution round the sun. Delicate measurements made by Edison PETTIT and Seth B. NICHOLSON at the Mount Wilson Observatory show that the heat on Mercury's sunlit side is so intense that it would cause lead and tin to melt. On the other face, plunged forever in the darkness of night, the temperature cannot be far above $-273°$ centigrade or absolute zero. Less rigorous conditions may exist in the "twilight zone", or region between day and night. Even so, there is every reason to believe that life as we know it cannot exist on Mercury.

Unlike Mercury, the planet Venus can be a most conspicuous object for many weeks. This is due in part to its size and distance from the sun – and hence from the earth. Its diameter of 7800 miles makes it far larger than Mercury and almost equal in size to the earth. Its average distance from the sun, 67,000,000 miles, brings it at certain times closer to the earth than any other natural planet. The minimum distance is 24,600,000 miles, or about 10,000,000 miles closer than we can ever come to Mars, but this gives no visual advantage since Venus is then at inferior conjunction and has its dark hemisphere turned towards us. Also important in connection with its brightness is the fact that it reflects nearly 60 per cent of the incoming sunlight.

Venus can attain a maximum elongation of about 46°, but greatest brilliance is achieved only about five weeks before and after inferior conjunction. The planet then appears as a crescent similar to that of the moon about five days from the time of new moon, and with the exception of the sun and moon becomes the brightest object in the sky. It can be seen in daylight and at night is capable of casting distinct shadows. The complete phase cycle or synodic period is about 584 days, or over twice the sidereal period of 225 days.

The visible surface of Venus is not that of the planet itself but the top of its cloud-laden atmosphere. Thick layers of opaque cloud entirely cover the lower regions and give the planet its

Venus as seen telescopically from the earth in each of the six positions shown in the previous illustration. The range in phase is associated with another in size (owing to varying distance which is more than 1 : 6 from full to new).

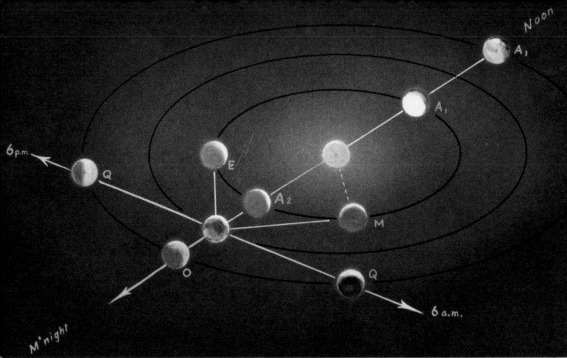

A superior planet, like Mars, can be visible all through the night when viewed from the earth. An inferior planet, like Venus, is seen only in the sun's neighbourhood and therefore never at or near midnight. It is most prominent as a "morning" or "evening star" just before sunrise or after sunset respectively.

snowy-white appearance. Sometimes faint and elusive dusky markings are seen and can be recorded on photographic plates sensitive to ultra-violet and infra-red radiation, but these patches are not permanent and clearly belong to the cloud mantle. Strangely enough, spectrographic studies have so far failed to detect either water vapor or oxygen. Carbon dioxide exists in amounts so large as to prevent life as we know it from existing on the planet's surface.

In 1954, as the result of photographs of Venus taken in violet light with the 82-inch reflector of the Yerkes and McDonald Observatories, Kuiper inferred that the equator of Venus is tilted about 32° from the plane of its orbit. The period of rotation remains uncertain, but recent spectrographic studies by Robert Richardson of the Mount Wilson and Palomar Observatories show that it is neither as short as 22 hours nor as long as 225 days as was previously suggested. The mean of 102 of the best observations gave a period of 14 days in the retrograde sense, or contrary to Venus's motion round the sun. Radio observations appear to support this result. In 1956, at Ohio State University, a series of brief bursts of radio noise from Venus were observed on a wavelength of 11 meters. These series of bursts each recurred about every 13 days.

With a diameter at its equator of 7927 miles, the earth is the fifth largest planet in the solar system. It is the only one which we know to be inhabited, and this because its atmosphere is sufficiently warm, humid and plentiful in gases essential to life. Between them nitrogen (78 per cent) and oxygen (21 per cent) make up the greater volume of the atmosphere. There is nearly one per cent by volume of argon, but the other gases, all chemically inert, are extremely rare. The atmosphere is at once a reservoir of water vapor, a heat blanket and regulator, and a shield against meteors, cosmic-ray particles and short-wave radiations. Yet although it is about 100 miles deep, it is breathable only to a height of about three miles, and clouds are usually restricted to heights below seven miles. At a height of 45 miles the air pressure and hence density (for constant temperature) are only about one ten thousandth of their surface values.

The earth has an average density $5\frac{1}{2}$ times that of water and is therefore the densest of all the planets. Since the mean density of the upper crust is less than three, that deep down must be more than $5\frac{1}{2}$. The crust has an average thickness of about 30 miles

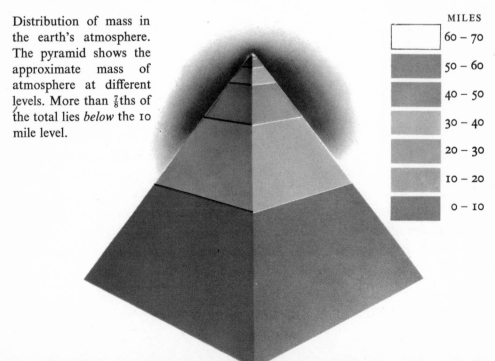

Distribution of mass in the earth's atmosphere. The pyramid shows the approximate mass of atmosphere at different levels. More than $\frac{7}{8}$ths of the total lies *below* the 10 mile level.

MILES

60 – 70

50 – 60

40 – 50

30 – 40

20 – 30

10 – 20

0 – 10

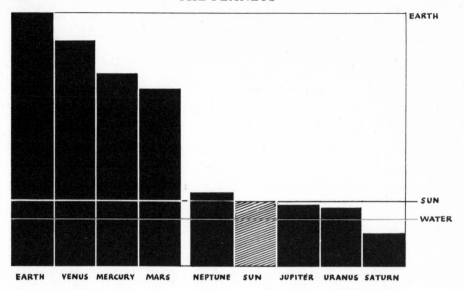

Block diagram showing the different average densities of the planets.

and floats on a hot and highly viscous liquid, or better, pseudo-liquid, so highly compressed as to assume many of the properties of a solid. The pressure increases with increasing depth, and within the central core (which probably consists of molten iron and nickel), reaches values over 2,000,000 tons per square foot.

The distribution of material on the earth's crust appears to be an important factor in determining the positions of the poles of the earth's axis of rotation. At one time, far back in geological history, the continents were probably nearer to each other than they are today, and to such an extent as to cause the north pole to be in the Pacific Ocean. Even now the poles are by no means fixed, but wander around mean positions, and this brings about corresponding variations in the latitudes and longitudes of places on the earth. The wandering is a complex one, but one element of the motion is known to be due to the seasonal melting and shifting of ice in the polar regions. The remarkable thing is not so much the fact that the poles wander but rather that, in view of the floating nature of the crust, they wander within an area only a few square yards in extent.

Next beyond the earth comes Mars, a world much smaller than our own and so distant that to the unaided eye it looks like a bright star distinguished by its orange-red hue. Mars has an average distance from the sun of about 142,000,000 miles, but this can vary either way by more than 26,000,000 miles. It takes nearly 687 days to circuit the sun, or nearly 780 days to do this relative to the moving earth. At intervals of approximately two years and two months, therefore, Mars makes a close approach to or OPPOSITION with the earth, its distance on these occasions varying from nearly 35,000,000 to 63,000,000 miles owing to the comparatively large eccentricity (0·093) of its orbit. Really close approaches occur at intervals of 15 or 17 years, the last being in 1956 when Mars came to within 34,600,000 miles from the earth. The planet then becomes a conspicuous object, second only to Venus in brilliancy, and most favorably placed for the telescopic study of its surface features.

Mars has a diameter just over 4200 miles and hence has only about a fourth of the surface area of the earth. Even at its closest, and when examined with a telescope magnifying about 70 times, Mars looks no larger than the full moon as seen with the naked eye. It is therefore by no means an easy planet to study, and what secrets it has revealed are the result of many years' careful and patient observation. One thing at least is known for sure: Mars has an atmosphere through which we can see the planet's comparatively flat surface and the grosser markings on that surface.

From a point near a sphere it is not possible to see across the full diameter of the sphere. A planet's diameter cannot therefore be measured directly.

A line bisecting angle A will meet the planets' center and form the hypotenuse of a right-angled triangle. Hence $R = d\tan\frac{1}{2}A$, and $2R$ = diameter of the planet = $2d\tan\frac{1}{2}A$.

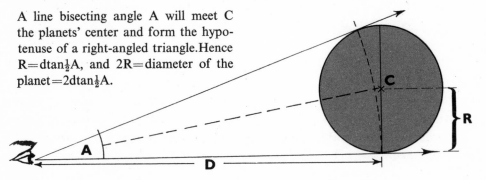

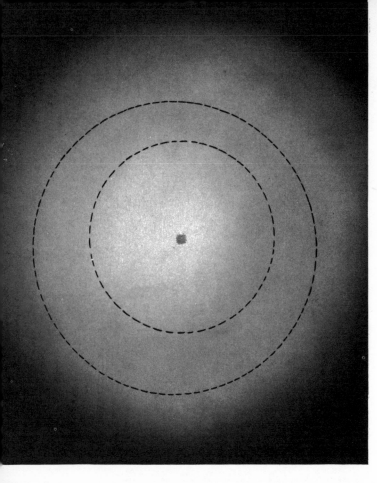

Comparison of the orbits of Mars (outer) and of the earth (inner).

The atmosphere of Mars is considerably thinner than the earth's – so thin that the pressure at surface level is probably equal to that found at a height of some 10 to 11 miles in our own atmosphere. It certainly contains carbon dioxide. Nitrogen may be plentiful, but oxygen and water vapor, two constituents so necessary to human life, appear to be almost absent. Yet although it is thin, the Martian atmosphere is not always quiescent. Sometimes the surface markings are obscured by yellowish patches which grow in size to cover large areas. They are generally considered to be clouds of dust whipped up by currents in the icy Martian air. These dust storms were unfortunately only too evident during the otherwise favorable opposition of 1956. Sometimes the surface details are veiled as if by haze or mist, while occasional whitish projections are seen on the limb which may well be high-altitude clouds of ice crystals.

The equator of Mars is inclined at nearly 24° to the plane of its orbit and it rotates on its axis once in about 24 hours 57 minutes. In these respects it is similar to the earth, but being farther from the sun, receives less heat than does the earth. At the equator the midday temperature may rise above freezing to about 10° centigrade. At sunrise or sunset it is well below zero, and at midnight may be quite beyond human endurance.

Mars reflects only about 15 per cent of the incident solar radiation. The telescope reveals that about two-thirds of its surface is reddish in color and that this part remains practically unchanged year after year. The reddish areas, especially on account of the dryness of the Martian atmosphere, are probably extensive dust plains comparable to the Painted Desert in Arizona. Rupert WILDT and others have suggested that the color arises from the presence of large quantities of iron oxide in the surface deposits, a feature which would account for the almost complete absence of free oxygen in the Martian atmosphere.

The remaining one-third consists of grayish-green patches and two white polar caps. In general the darkish areas undergo

Despite its brilliance a polar cap of Mars has sometimes been completely obscured for many days. This may be due to dust clouds sweeping over the cap.

changes in both extent and intensity of hue. They are certainly not expanses of water as was at first believed. Their changes appear to have a seasonal basis and to be related to changes in the appearance of the polar caps. As the north-polar cap is turned more and more towards the sun, in the northern spring and summer, it shrinks from an area about 3000 miles across to one with a diameter less than 200 miles. According to some observers a corresponding wave of darkening moves slowly southwards towards the Martian equator, suggestive of the response of vegetation to warmth and moisture. If, as seems most likely, the polar caps are layers of snow, the melting snow provides water which in either liquid or vapor form reaches the thirsty temperate and equatorial regions. Meanwhile, the south-polar cap increases in size, but when spring and summer return to the southern hemisphere the wave of darkening moves northwards.

Not all astronomers agree that the changes in the darkish areas are seasonal or that they are related to those which take place in

The reason for the apparent retrogression of a superior planet near the time of opposition.

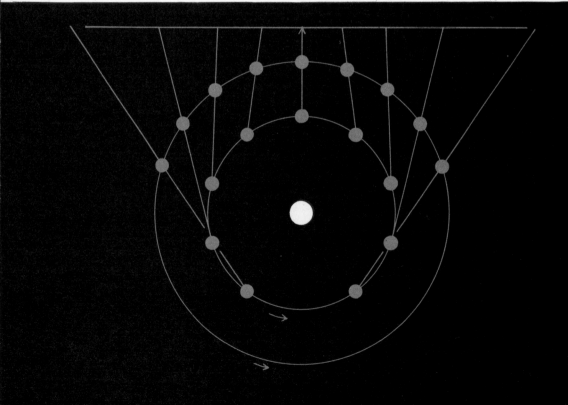

the polar caps. Indeed, some of the features undergo very little change and appear to be permanent in both hue and intensity of hue. The caps vary too much in size to be continents of ice similar to those on earth and are probably no more than layers of snow a few inches thick. One obvious difficulty is to account for the passage of water to and from the polar regions – unless, of course, one accepts the idea of artificial waterways, the so-called "canals on Mars".

In 1877 the Italian astronomer Giovanni SCHIAPARELLI detected narrow dusky streaks on the face of Mars which he called "canali" or channels. This interpretation of the markings was developed by the American astronomer, Percival LOWELL. Using large telescopes, Lowell made an intensive study of Mars during the opposition of 1894–5 and concluded that the channels were actually irrigation canals, designed and built by intelligent Martians to convey water from the melting polar caps to the arid equatorial regions.

Lowell depicted the "canali" as fine straight lines and believed that the vegetation, extending away some 20 or so miles on either side of a canal, rendered it visible from the earth. As popularly interpreted at the time, the discovery of these "canals" set off considerable speculation and controversy, and Mars became the most talked-about planet besides the earth. So far, only the broader "canali" have been photographed, and photographic plates have yet to reveal a network of fine straight lines, but this does not mean that it does not exist. Recent results, however, largely discourage rather than support Lowell's observations, and many observers consider that the canals are illusory. The eye, they suggest, unconsciously joins together separate surface details which in themselves are too small to be resolved individually but which collectively appear to form lines and a network of lines.

Mars has two tiny satellites, first seen during the favorable opposition of 1877 by Asaph HALL with the 26-inch refractor of the Naval Observatory in Washington. Deimos, the outer one, is only about five miles in diameter, while Phobos, the inner one, is about 10 miles across. Deimos, at an average distance of 12,500 miles from the surface of Mars, makes one revolution in just over

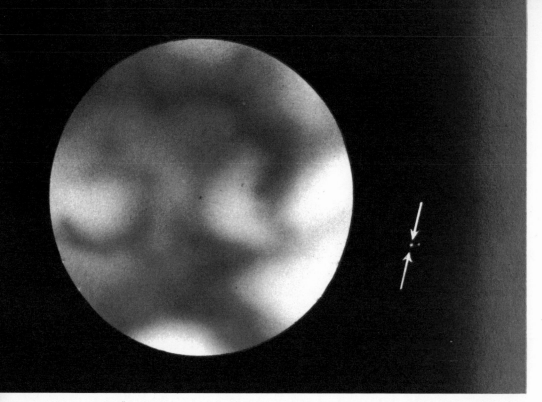

The tiny Martian moon Phobos (arrowed) at its greatest possible separation from the planet. On the same scale the earth would appear nearly twice as large as Mars and the moon would be about 150 times as distant as Phobos.

50 hours. Since this is only about six hours longer than the rotation period of Mars, Deimos appears to move but slowly across the Martian sky, being above the horizon for a place near the equator for more than 60 hours. Phobos, at a mean distance of only 3760 miles above the Martian surface, flies round the planet once in about seven hours 39 minutes. It therefore moves faster than an observer at or near the equator and not only appears to rise in the west and set in the east but stays above the horizon for only about three hours. In these respects Phobos is unique – it is the only known natural satellite whose period of revolution is shorter than the rotation period of its primary.

Leaving Mars, and moving outwards from the sun to a distance of about 484,000,000 miles, we come to the orbit of Jupiter, the largest and most massive of the planets. At this immense distance

The appearance of Mars during spring in the southern hemisphere.

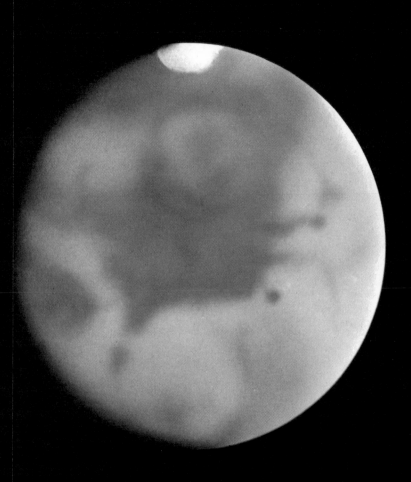

T. Maloney, F.R.A.S.

Jupiter takes almost 12 of our years to circuit the sun, and therefore on the average spends about a year in each of the 12 constellations of the zodiac. It is also feebly illuminated by the sun, but
because of its size and high reflectivity, is surpassed in brightness
among the planets only by Venus and sometimes by Mars at its
brightest. Like Mars and the other so-called "superior planets"
whose orbits lie outside the earth's, Jupiter can be seen at all
hours of the night. Like Mars, it is at its brightest when at or near
opposition; it then presents a definite disk when examined with
quite a small telescope or a pair of BINOCULARS.

At its equator Jupiter has a diameter of 88,700 miles. Its
volume is so great that it could contain over 1300 globes each the
size of the earth. The period of rotation at the equator is remarkably short – only 9 hours 50 minutes – which represents a speed of
28,000 miles an hour. Because of this Jupiter has a marked polar
flattening and a polar diameter of only 82,800 miles.

The telescope shows that Jupiter's broad disk is crossed by an
array of dusky bands or belts spread roughly parallel to the
planet's equator. These belts are clearly swirling cloud-banks so
dense and deep that they prevent our ever seeing the planet's solid
(or perhaps liquid) surface. Changes in their details and general
appearance indicate highly turbulent conditions, although many
of the markings, like the GREAT RED SPOT, are semi-permanent.
The Great Red Spot is the name given to a large oval patch which
grew into prominence in 1878 and which is still partly and faintly
visible. Spectroscopic studies reveal that Jupiter's atmosphere is
without doubt completely different from the earth's. Not only is it
considerably cooler, but it seems to consist of hydrogen, helium
and deadly methane gas in which float clouds of crystals of
frozen ammonia. For life to exist in such conditions, its form and
constitution must be very different from those found on the earth.

In 1955 Bernard Burke and Kenneth L. Franklin of the Car-
negie Institution of Washington discovered that Jupiter emits intense bursts of radio energy. These bursts are sudden and highly
intense, and have since been found to originate from a particular
area or areas in Jupiter's south temperate belt. The cause of the
radio emission is unknown. Lightning discharges have been

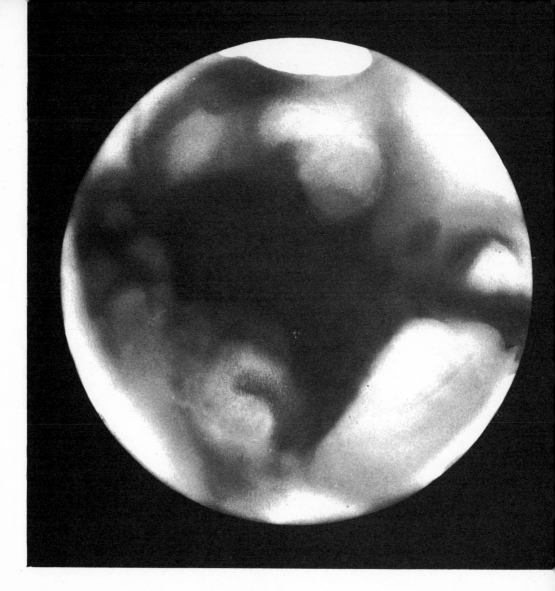

The planet Mars.

suggested, but if these are the cause their energy contents must be fantastically higher than those of terrestrial lightning.

Jupiter has twelve known satellites of which the eight inner-most revolve in the same direction as the planet rotates. Of the four discovered by Galileo in 1610, Ganymede and Callisto are each larger than the moon and have diameters of 3000 and 2800 miles respectively. The other two, Io and Europa, are slightly

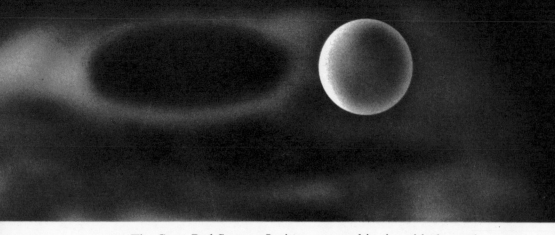

The Great Red Spot on Jupiter compared in size with the earth.

smaller than the moon. All four move in the plane of Jupiter's equator and frequently pass in front of and behind its disk. When they pass in front they cast observable round shadows on the cloud belts of Jupiter. When they pass behind and enter Jupiter's shadow they are said to be eclipsed. The other eight satellites are comparatively small bodies; they range in diameter from 100 miles to only 12 miles and in period of revolution from nearly 12 hours for the innermost to 758 days for the outermost.

Moving far beyond the orbit of Jupiter is Saturn, the most distant of the five naked-eye planets known since antiquity. Saturn's mean distance from the sun is nearly 890 million miles, or just over $9\frac{1}{2}$ times the corresponding distance for the earth. Its year

The four "Galilean" satellites of Jupiter provide an interesting spectacle as seen from the earth. The solid arrow points to the sun; the open arrow points to the earth.

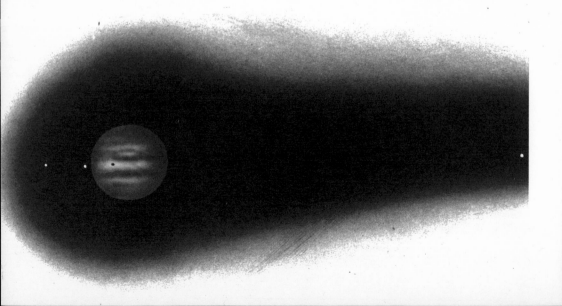

William Herschel.

consists of nearly 29½ of our years, but the synodic period is only 378 days, or 21 days shorter than Jupiter's.

Saturn is the most spectacular of all the planets. Its great yellowish globe, 75,100 miles across at the equator, is girdled by three magnificent rings. The innermost ring, with its inside edge about 9000 miles from Saturn, is dusky and transparent enough to enable the body of Saturn to be seen through it. The second or middle ring is broad and bright. It is separated from the outer ring by a dark space known as the CASSINI DIVISION in honor of the astronomer Giovanni Domenico CASSINI who first detected its presence in 1675. The outermost ring, with an outside diameter of about 170,000 miles, is about half as wide as the middle one.

Jupiter and the four " Galilean " satellites.

While the overall width of this splendid system is nearly 38,000 miles, its thickness appears to be no more than about 10 miles. Small wonder, therefore, that when at 15-year intervals the rings are presented edge-on to an observer on the earth, they appear to vanish altogether, even when they are viewed through the largest telescopes.

The rings were once thought to be solid, but in 1895 James Keeler at the Allegheny Observatory studied them spectrographically and found that not only do they rotate about Saturn's globe, but also obey Kepler's Laws, for the inner sections rotate faster than the outer sections. No solid ring could rotate in this way. Saturn's rings probably consist of myriads of particles of rock and/or ice whose total mass is perhaps less than a hundredth of that of our moon.

Saturn is also unusual in that its average density is only 0·72 that of water. For its size it is the lightest of all the planets – so light that it could float on water. In view of this low average density, and if, as Wildt has suggested, Saturn has a solid rocky core, the core must be a small one. Through the telescope we see only the top of Saturn's cloud-laden atmosphere, and this appears to be far less turbulent than Jupiter's. Parallel belts can be discerned, but they are less prominent and detailed than those of Jupiter. The rotation period in the equatorial zone is no more than about 10 hours, 15 minutes, and sufficiently short to give the globe a marked polar flattening.

Saturn, like Jupiter, appears to have no heat of its own, and its surface temperature is no more than about $-150°$ centigrade. At this temperature much of the ammonia is frozen out of the gaseous mantle; methane is even more plentiful than on Jupiter. Under these conditions human life could not possibly exist.

Saturn controls a family of ten satellites, all of which lie outside the rings. By far the largest is Titan, a body about equal in size to Mercury and Ganymede. Phoebe, the most distant satellite, is the only one to have retrograde motion; its diameter of about 150 miles makes it the smallest member of the family. With ten satellites continually changing their places, and the magnificent rings stretching like luminous arches from horizon to horizon,

Saturn's sky above the layers of cloud must be splendid indeed.

Far beyond the orbit of Saturn travel the three planets Uranus, Neptune, and Pluto, all of which require a telescope for their successful observation. Under favorable conditions Uranus appears as a star of the sixth magnitude and can therefore just be seen with the unaided eye. It was discovered by William Herschel in 1781 while he was making a survey of the heavens with a small home-made reflecting telescope. Those who had seen it before had mistaken it for a faint fixed star, and even Herschel at first thought that it was a comet. Further observations soon revealed that it was a planet – and, moreover, a major one, so distant from the sun as to require 84 years for one complete revolution. Its mean distance from the sun is about 1800 million miles; seen from this distance the sun would appear to be hardly larger than a brilliant star.

The diameter of Uranus is not known with certainty but is considered to be about 31,000 miles. Its physical condition is probably similar to that of Jupiter and Saturn. The actual surface is hidden from view by a mantle of clouds of methane. Nearly all the ammonia must be in a frozen state, but free hydrogen and helium are undoubtedly present. Spectrographic observations

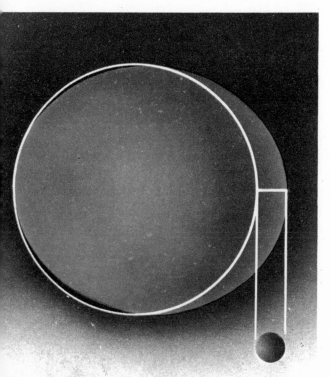

Low average density and high speed of rotation combine to flatten the globe of Saturn and to make it the least spherical of all the planets. Here its shape is compared with the outline of a sphere (white line). The earth (to the same scale) is introduced to show the immense extent of the equatorial bulge.

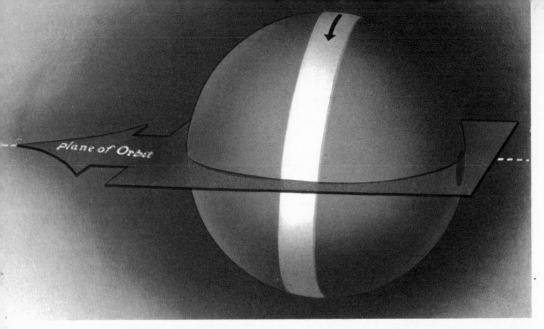

Almost the entire surface of Uranus has "tropical" conditions. Only a narrow zone round the planet's equator (white) fails at some time or another to experience the "midnight sun". Only a tiny area at each pole (blue) fails to experience a sun virtually overhead at some time during a Uranian year.

show that the axial spin is completed once in $10\frac{3}{4}$ hours and is therefore quite rapid; the axis itself lies almost in the plane of the orbit of revolution.

Uranus has five satellites. They move in orbits which lie in the plane of the planet's equator and which are therefore steeply inclined to its orbit of revolution. They are all comparatively small bodies, the largest (Titania) being only 600 miles across. Sir William Herschel discovered two of them (Titania and Oberon) in 1787, and William LASSELL discovered two more (Ariel and Umbriel) in 1851. The fifth and innermost satellite (Miranda), with a diameter probably under 100 miles, was discovered in 1948 by Kuiper on photographic plates taken with the 82-inch reflector of the Yerkes and McDonald Observatories.

The discovery of Neptune ranks as one of the greatest triumphs of mathematical astronomy. By 1845 it had become evident that the observed positions of Uranus in the sky did not agree with

The planet Jupiter.

T. Maloney FRAS

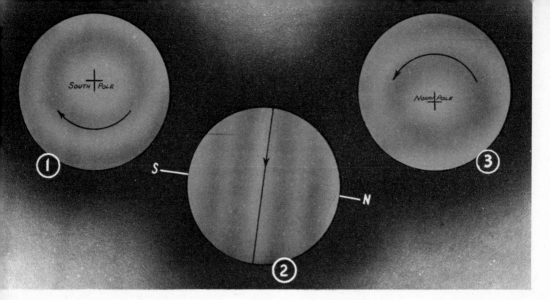

Uranus as seen from the sun.
1, Southern "summer" : 2, "spring" : 3, northern "summer".

those computed from tables of its motion prepared by Alexis Bouvard of Paris. The discrepancies pointed to the existence of a great planet far beyond the orbit of Uranus. After long and tedious mathematical investigations, Urbain LEVERRIER in France and John Adams in England independently determined the approximate mass, motion and location of the disturbing object. Neptune was first picked up on the night of September 23, 1846, by Johann Galle of Berlin, who found it within 52 minutes of arc of the predicted position.

At a mean distance of about 2797 million miles from the sun, Neptune takes nearly 165 years to complete one trip around the sun. As seen through even large telescopes it presents a small uniform disk and shows no apparent flattening. Its diameter, difficult to determine, is about 28,000 miles; Neptune is therefore slightly smaller than Uranus. As with Uranus, the main constituent of its atmosphere appears to be methane.

Neptune has two satellites. Triton, with a diameter of about 2500 miles, was discovered by Lassell within a month after the discovery of Neptune itself. Its motion is retrograde in that it moves in an orbit inclined at an angle well in excess of 90° to the planet's equator. In this respect it is similar to four of Jupiter's satellites and to Phoebe, the outermost satellite of Saturn. Nereid, Neptune's outer satellite, was discovered by Kuiper in 1949. Its diameter is only about 200 miles and the eccentricity of its orbit (0·76) is by far the largest known for any natural satellite.

Pluto, the most distant known planet, was not discovered until 1930, and then as a result of a close study of apparent irregularities in the motion of Neptune. It was found photographically by Clyde Tombaugh of the Lowell Observatory, Flagstaff, Arizona. Although its mean distance from the sun is 3666 million miles, the comparatively high eccentricity of its orbit (0·248, the largest among the planets) brings it at times closer to us than Neptune. The greater part of its 248-year period, however, is spent beyond the path of Neptune, and during this time it moves out to an aphelion distance of about 4500 million miles.

Recent measurements by Kuiper and Henri Camichel indicate that Pluto is slightly larger than Mars. If this is the case, Pluto must be almost as dense as the earth and is in this respect quite unlike the other outer planets. There is probably little or no atmosphere, for at a temperature of almost absolute zero any of Pluto's free methane would be in the liquid or solid state. Dark, barren and frigid, Pluto is surely the loneliest member of the sun's remarkable family of planets.

A, Jupiter; B, Neptune; C, Saturn; shown as black disks to indicate the sizes which these planets would have if their average densities were each the same as that of the earth, the densest member of the nine major planets.

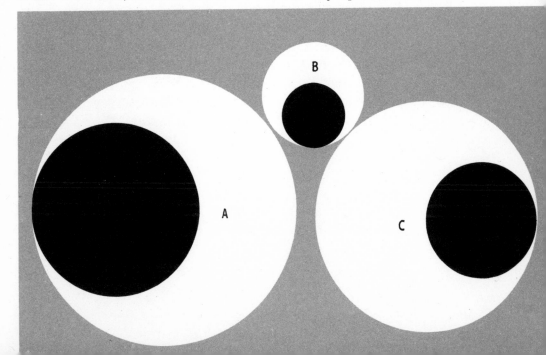

In 1772 the German astronomer Johann BODE drew attention
to a curious numerical relationship between the distances of the
planets from the sun. This relationship, originally formulated by
Johann D. TITIUS in 1766, became known as BODE'S LAW, and
pointed to the existence of a planet in the great gap of about
350,000,000 miles between the orbits of Mars and Jupiter. A
group of observers in Germany thereupon decided to search for
the unknown planet, but they were forestalled in its discovery by
Giuseppe PIAZZI, director of the Palermo Observatory in Sicily.

On the night of January 1, 1801, while making routine observations for a catalogue of star positions, Piazzi came across a star-
like object which changed its position night after night relative to
the "fixed" stars. Illness unfortunately prevented him continuing
his observations beyond six weeks, and when he was at last able to
return to his telescope he could find no trace of the moving
"star". The observations he had secured, however, enabled the
German mathematician Johann GAUSS to determine its orbit and
predict where it might be found. Hence it came about that Piazzi's
wanderer was redetected only about $\frac{1}{2}°$ from the predicted position and on December 31, 1801, that is exactly a year after its
discovery.

The new object, named Ceres, proved to be a small planet
moving between the orbits of Mars and Jupiter, and at a distance
from the sun which conveniently agreed with that predicted by
Bode's Law. Yet its diameter is so small (only about 480 miles)
that it has become known not as a planet but as an ASTEROID or
minor planet. Nor is Ceres the only object of its type. In March,
1802, Heinrich OLBERS, a member of the "celestial police" organ-
ized for planet detection in Germany, discovered a second asteroid which he named Pallas. Harding, another member of the German group, discovered a third (Juno) in 1804, and Olbers found a
fourth (Vesta) in 1807. All three are smaller than Ceres and have

Three aspects of Saturn. *Top:* a plane of rings inclined about 14° (to the line of
sight): *center:* a plane of rings inclined about $3\frac{1}{2}°$: *lower:* rings open to their
greatest extent.

T. Maloney FRAS

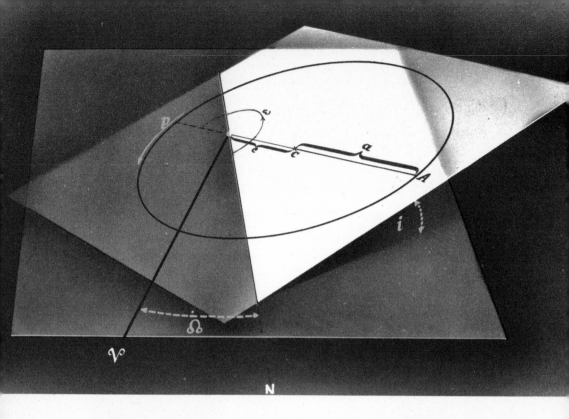

The elements of a planet's orbit. a, semi-major axis: e, eccentricity: i, inclination: Ω, longitude of the node: ω, argument of perihelion. The symbol ♈ indicates the direction of the "First point of Aries".

diameters of 300, 240, and 120 miles respectively. A fifth was not added until 1845, when Karl HENCKE discovered Astraea, a body only 60 miles across.

By 1890, the number of known asteroids had grown to 300, and after that year rose rapidly as a result of photographic methods of discovery introduced by Max WOLF of Heidelberg. The principle underlying these methods is to move a photographic telescope of wide field in the usual way so that it follows the march of the stars across the sky. During the time of exposure the stars are reproduced on the photographic plate as round patches, but the asteroid, moving all the time relative to the stars, gives rise to a short line or trail and is thereby readily detected on the developed plates. Over 1500 have now had their orbits determined, but this number is believed to be only a small fraction of the total number in existence. In size they range from Ceres, a fly-weight world

which may be spherical in shape, down to irregular masses only a
mile or so in diameter.

Studies of the periods of revolution of the asteroids show that
the average period is about $4\frac{1}{2}$ years and that most of them fall
within the range three years to six years. Their periods are by no
means uniformly distributed but tend to avoid values which are a
half, a third, and other small simple fractions of the period of
Jupiter. The orbits which would correspond to these periods are
called resonant orbits, and appear to arise largely because of the
perturbing action of Jupiter's great mass. These Jovian perturbations, operating over a long period, have so to speak shuffled the

The orbits of Neptune and Pluto. Although Pluto is the most distant planet
from the sun it can come nearer to the sun at perihelion than Neptune ever can.

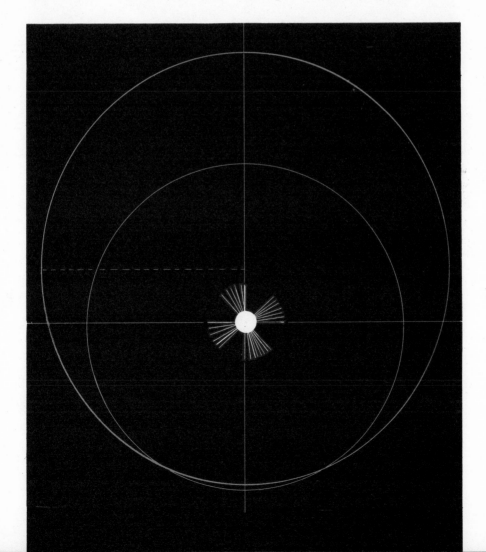

View of Saturn along a direction perpendicular to the plane of its rings.

asteroids into specific groups of orbits. On the other hand, and strangely enough, there are groups with periods of eight and nine years, that is, with periods two-thirds and three-quarters of the period of Jupiter. There is even a group, called the Trojans, whose mean period differs but little from that of Jupiter itself.

It has been suggested that the asteroids had a common origin in a planet which exploded or was otherwise disrupted. Owing to the long-term perturbations of Jupiter (and to a far lesser extent to those of Saturn), the orbits of the fragments underwent considerable change and must now have little or no resemblance to their former characteristics. There are, however, certain combinations of the orbital elements which appear to have remained appreciably unaltered over many million years. From a study of these, S. Hirayama of Tokyo found traces of five groups or families, the members of each of which probably originated from a single mass. On the other hand, the asteroids may have originally existed not as a single planet but as a fairly uniform band of dust which tended to merge into a single condensation but which subdivided before reaching final consolidation.

Most asteroids are scattered in orbits which lie between those of the Mars and Jupiter. Some asteroids come inside the earth's orbit and others move outside Jupiter's orbit.

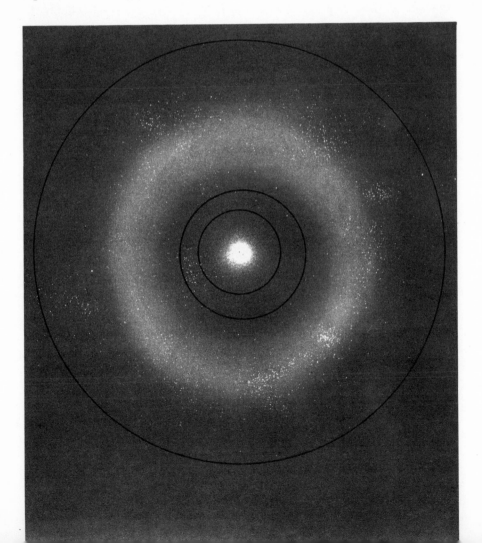

Although the asteroids in general occupy the zone between the orbits of Mars and Jupiter, a few have orbits outside these limits. One of particular interest is Eros, discovered photographically in 1898 by Karl WITT of Berlin. At a mean distance from the sun of about 136,000,000 miles, Eros has a sidereal period of only $1\frac{3}{4}$ years. Its orbit has an eccentricity of 0·22 and crosses inside that of Mars, bringing it at times quite close to the earth. On the most favorable occasions Eros can come to within 14,000,000 miles of the earth, but oppositions as close as this are rare. One occurred in 1894, four years before Eros was discovered.

During a less favorable approach in 1931, when Eros was about 16,000,000 miles away, it was widely and intensively observed in order to determine more accurately the solar parallax, or measure of the distance of the sun. Basically the method was to measure, relative to the fixed stars, the displacement of Eros as seen from two different places on the earth. The known separation of the two places constituted a base line, and this, considered together with the corresponding angle of displacement of Eros, led directly to a value for its distance from the earth. The revolution period of Eros was already accurately determined, so by using Kepler's third law of planetary motion, astronomers were able to derive the mean distance of the earth from the sun. As a result of the 1931 observations the solar parallax was found to be 8·790″ with a probable error of 0·001″, which corresponds to a mean distance of 93,005,000 miles.

When at its closest, Eros appears like a star of about magnitude seven, but at less favorable oppositions it can be little more than magnitude 11 or 12. During opposition (and presumably throughout the entire orbital period) it undergoes periodic variations in brightness which are almost certainly due to its rotation. There is now no doubt that Eros has an elongated shape; that while its long axis is about 14 miles its short axis is only about five miles. In February, 1931, while using the 26-inch refractor of the Union Observatory at Johannesburg, W. H. van den Bos and W. S. Finsen actually saw the elongated form of Eros and assessed the period of rotation (and of light variation) to be five hours, 17 minutes.

Eros is not the only one to come near the earth. In April, 1932,
K. REINMUTH of Heidelberg discovered a rapidly moving asteroid later named Apollo. When its orbit was computed it was
found to move for part of its period within the orbit of Venus and
to have approached as close as 2,000,000 miles from the earth.
Then in February, 1936, E. DELPORTE of Uccle detected Adonis,
an asteroid which passed by the earth at a distance of about
1,000,000 miles, and in October, 1937, Reinmuth discovered
Hermes, a tiny body thrown into such an orbit that its minimum
distance from the earth was no more than twice that of the moon.
Like Apollo, both Adonis and Hermes move in orbits which cross
inside that of Venus.

The asteroid with the most extraordinary orbit is Icarus, first
detected by Walter F. BAADE in June, 1949, on a photograph
taken with the 48-inch Schmidt camera on Palomar Mountain.
With an exceptionally high eccentricity of 0·83, the orbit of Icarus
brings it at perihelion to within 18,000,000 miles from the sun, or
about halfway between the mean distance of Mercury and the
sun. It then sweeps far out beyond the orbit of Mars but returns
to perihelion after only 409 days.

The minor planet Eros has an elongated shape, with its long axis about 14
miles and its short axis about 5 miles in length.

Another body with a highly elongated orbit is Hidalgo, whose period of 14 years is the longest yet known. With an orbital eccentricity of 0·65, Hidalgo moves out at aphelion to the mean distance of Saturn and at perihelion to a position between the orbits of the earth and Mars.

While the orbits of some asteroids cross those of the earth and neighboring planets, the chances of collisions are extremely remote. It must be remembered in this connection that they are mostly tiny bodies and that many of them have orbits of high inclination. Indeed, Hidalgo's orbit is inclined at just over 42° to the ecliptic, but this is exceptionally high: most of them are less than 16°. It is not, however, outside the bounds of possibility that in the distant future an as yet undetected asteroid of the nature of a flying mountain may pass perilously close to the earth or even score a direct hit. If ever the latter occurred, and with a body a mile or so in diameter, it would devastate an enormous area and send intense shock-waves to every part of the earth.

The planets, drawn to the same scale for the purposes of comparison, are superimposed on part of the sun.

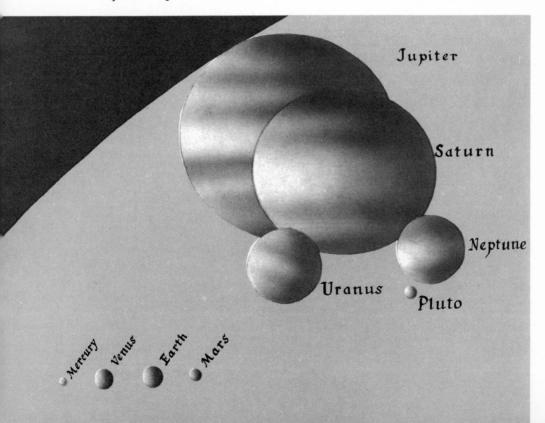

6. Comets and meteors

While Pluto is the most distant known planet, the sun's far-flung family contains many bodies which move out to much greater distances. These are the comets, most if not all of which are members of the solar system. Kepler thought that they were more numerous than fish in the sea, an idea which later researches and over three hundred years of telescopic observation have done much to substantiate. J. H. OORT, for instance, considers that the sun is enveloped in a vast cloud of comets which stretches out to about half the distance of the nearest star. In any case, many comets are certainly periodic, that is, they move in elliptical paths about the sun and reappear in our skies at fairly regular intervals. Halley's Comet for example, has a period of about 75 years: its most recent return was in 1910 and it is scheduled to reappear in 1986. Yet its period is a short one compared with those of a thousand years and more for comets which move out to at least twenty times the distance of Neptune from the sun. Many comets on the other hand have comparatively short periods of 10 years and less, and in the main move within the confines of Jupiter's orbit. One fairly faint object, Encke's Comet, has a period of only 3·3 years, the shortest yet known.

Unlike the planets, most comets pursue highly elongated orbits. They move in accordance with Kepler's Laws and by the Law of Equal Areas travel with greatest speed when near the sun or at perihelion and slowest when at aphelion. At perihelion Halley's Comet moves within the orbits of Mercury and Venus and can therefore on occasion make quite close approaches to the earth. Indeed, on May 20, 1910, the comet came so near that its tail swept across the earth, but without causing anyone the slightest inconvenience. At aphelion it is well beyond the orbit of Neptune, where because of its motion in so eccentric an orbit, it spends more than half of its period of 75 years.

Since comets in general move in this way they invariably appear suddenly in the sky and undergo night-to-night changes in position against the background of stars. In addition, certain comets change markedly in form, size and brightness as they approach the sun, all of which tends to make them very conspicuous. At its last appearance Halley's Comet, true to custom, grew a great

A comet in that part of its orbit which brings it near the sun. As it approaches the sun the comet brightens and grows a tail which tends to be directed away from the sun.

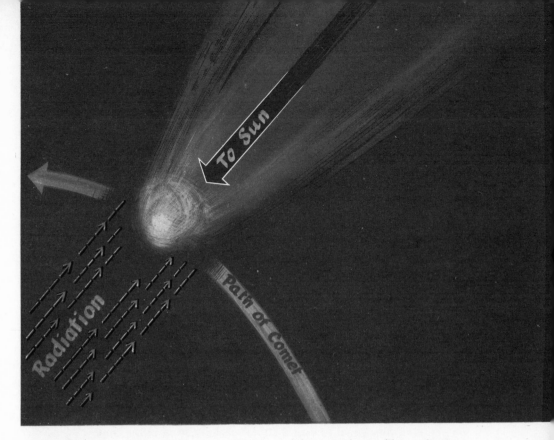

The structure of a comet. Its head consists of a bright central part (the nucleus) surrounded by a haze of light (the coma). From the head, and under pressure of the sun's radiation, streams the tail.

tail which in mid-May of 1910, stretched across the sky like a searchlight beam. Its maximum length is said to have been nearly 140° of arc, which corresponded to an actual distance of about 93,000,000 miles.

The word "comet" is derived from a Greek word meaning "long-haired" and refers to the long streaming tail or tails of these objects. In early times comets were classed as meteors and were supposed to be of the nature of burning torches suspended high in the atmosphere. For the superstitious they were omens of disaster. Hence when Halley's Comet in A.D. 66 appeared high over Jerusalem it was likened to a fiery sword of correction – a symbol of all the suffering which the city was about to experience at the hands of Titus. On another of its returns, in April, 1066, Halley's Comet seemed to hover over England like a great demon star and was

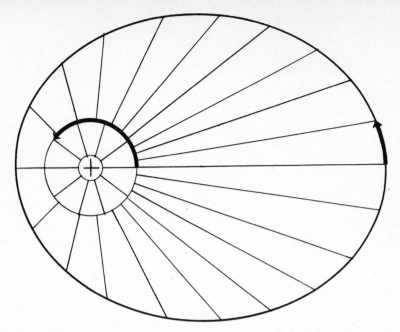

A comet's orbit (e=o·6) is divided into 20 "equal area" segments to show the distances traveled in equal periods of time. The planet's orbit, which is circular (e=o), is at a mean distance from the sun only $\frac{1}{4}$ as great. The planet's speed is constant. The arrow lengths show the respective distances covered by the comet and the planet when the comet is most distant from the sun (+) and over a period of time equal to $\frac{1}{20}$th the total orbital period of the comet.

said to foretell the success of Norman arms and the death of Harold. In 1759, when Halley's assertion that the comets of 1531, 1607, 1682 (and probably that of 1456) were one and the same object was so triumphantly verified, comets were still being blamed for the misfortunes of humanity. Even as late as 1910, according to an English newspaper report, "many people crowded on the sea-front at Oporto, Portugal, in order to see the comet. As they watched they crossed themselves in fear". This reference is not to Halley's Comet but to the great daylight Comet 1910 I, that is, to the first comet to have perihelion passage in that year. In another report dated January 26, 1910, we read: "The great cold now prevailing in Russia and the floods in France are ascribed to the comet's influence, while cholera, plague and revolution are commonly expected to result from its appearance."

A comet is now usually discovered long before it approaches naked eye visibility. It appears in the telescope or on the photographic plate as a diffuse patch and may or may not possess

NUCLEUS. The nucleus takes the form of a brighter and more condensed part which has a stellar appearance and generally lies towards the edge nearest the sun. The hazy area around the nucleus is called the coma, and most comets never seem to leave the coma or coma-with-nucleus form. They remain telescopic objects and far outnumber naked-eye comets of which only about 20 to 30 appear each century. On the other hand many telescopic comets develop tails but still remain below naked-eye visibility.

According to Fred L. WHIPPLE, the coma is a loose globular swarm of meteoric particles and dust, while the nucleus is a porous agglomeration of frozen gases and metallic grains. Spectrograms of bright comets invariably show a faint continuous background on which are superimposed bright lines and bands. The background arises from sunlight reflected by the comet while the lines are emission lines formed by hydrocarbons and chemical compounds containing carbon, nitrogen, oxygen and hydrogen. The molecules of these gases are thought to be in a state of FLUORESCENCE, that is, they selectively absorb certain parts of the incident solar radiation and re-emit them at longer wavelengths. When a comet is remote from the sun these gases probably all exist in the solid state and take the form of frozen lumps of ammonia, water and hydrocarbons.

The spectra differ in detail with different comets. Some, like that of Comet Arend-Roland 1957, contain the two yellow emission lines of atomic sodium, while emission lines due to iron and nickel atoms were observed in the spectrum of Comet 1882 II. During its perihelion passage the latter comet almost grazed the sun, being briefly within 300,000 miles of the solar surface and enduring heat so intense that the nucleus must have reached a temperature of at least 4000° centigrade. Had this been sustained over several hours it would have evaporated small nickel-iron particles and large quantities of the frozen gases. Yet the nucleus did not disappear – instead, it broke into several parts which remained visible until the comet was lost to view.

When a large comet approaches the sun a nebulous appendage or tail grows from the coma. This tail increases in length as the comet approaches and passes perihelion, and sometimes reaches

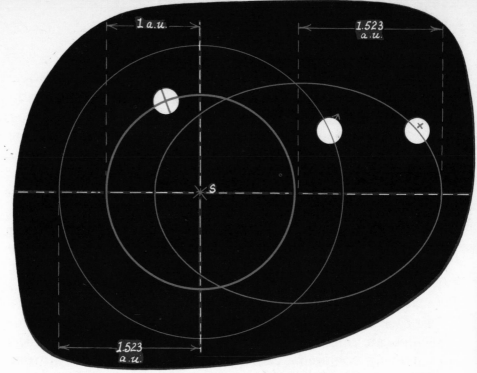

The two concentric circular orbits represent a simplification of the sun – earth – Mars system. The "oval" orbit to the right is cometary in form but has a semi-major axis exactly equal to that of Mars. It would therefore have an exactly equal period and always come to opposition in the same part of the Martian sky.

magnificent proportions. The coma and nucleus are then referred to as the head of the comet and to the unaided eye look like a bright but hazy star. The head contracts as the tail grows and at times assumes the appearance of a series of concentric luminous shells. Apparently the material in the nucleus is volatilized by the sun's heat and driven outwards to form a long streaming tail. In length the tail may be from 5,000,000 to 100,000,000 miles: that of the great comet of 1811 was upwards of 100,000,000 miles long and about 15,000,000 miles wide. The tail need not necessarily be single. One comet, the great comet of 1744, had at one stage as many as six separate tails.

Despite its enormous size a comet's tail is an extremely flimsy affair. It is far more tenuous than the finest cloud and is more nearly equivalent to a vacuum. When a comet passes between us and the stars the latter still remain clearly visible through both the coma and the tail, a fact first recorded by Seneca. The particles of the tail must therefore be extremely small and widely separated. As a general rule the tail or tails are always directed away from the sun. This suggests that the tail material is being pushed away from the head by radiation pressure. It is now well established that light behaves as if it possesses mass and is capable of exerting a pressure. When applied to the small particles in a comet's tail this pressure could well be several hundred times the opposing force of gravity. Even gas MOLECULES would, by selectively absorbing the radiation falling on them, be repelled, but there are good reasons for thinking that radiation pressure and selective absorption are not the only two forces involved.

The material in the tail does not, of course, collect there, for the attraction of the head is too weak to retain the matter sent out. The cometary head therefore loses mass every time it visits the sun and wastes away until all its substance is scattered over an immense region. Yet in spite of this wear and tear, Halley's Comet has made trips round the sun for at least 2000 years and still in 1910 produced a splendid tail.

The tails of many comets have shown rapid variations not only in structure but also in form. Morehouse's Comet of 1908 was remarkable in both respects, and photographs of its tail showed a number of unexpected and quite dramatic transformations. The tail had a decidedly patchy and ragged appearance, and the knots and wisps in it showed every evidence of an overall outward motion. Another remarkable comet was Comet 1925 II, a faint object discovered photographically by Schwassmann and Wachmann of Hamburg in 1927. This has been known to undergo a hundredfold increase in brightness in a few days, despite the fact that its entire orbit lies between those of Jupiter and Saturn. The greatest outburst appears to have been that which occurred sometime between early December, 1945, and late January, 1946. The magnitude then changed from 18 to 9·4, a change equivalent to a 2700 times increase in brightness. Equally unaccountable is the way this comet can change in a few days from a star-like object to a diffuse round coma.

Comet Arend-Roland developed a remarkable sunward tail or anti-tail. This anti-tail appeared towards the end of April, 1957, just two weeks after the comet's closest approach to the sun.

Within a few days the strange tail, or "beard", turned more and more towards the sun and at the same time narrowed to appear like a thin luminous spike. On May 1 this spike had practically vanished. These appearances arose because the comet possessed a flat and somewhat fan-shaped secondary tail. On April 25 the earth moved into the plane of this tail which consequently appeared as a thin, bright spike.

Nearly all the mass of a comet resides in the nucleus and even this is small by planetary standards. In all probability the mass of even a large comet is less than a millionth part that of the earth. In July, 1770, Lexell's Comet came to within 1,500,000 miles of the earth without affecting the earth's motion in any way. On the other hand there are numerous examples of a planet having effectively perturbed a comet's motion. Lexell's Comet had a period of $5\frac{1}{2}$ years but after its close approach to Jupiter in 1779 was so strongly affected that it has never been seen again. This is no doubt an example of a planet's perturbing influence changing a comet's orbit to one that does not bring it near the sun or earth where it is bright enough to be observed.

It is therefore clear that comets do not move solely under the influence of the sun's attraction and that the major planets can produce variations in their orbital elements. This was known to Halley, who realized that his prediction of the return of the comet of 1682 was of necessity an approximation. The time of its perihelion passage was in fact delayed by planetary influence, whereas its close approach to Jupiter in 1835 had an opposite effect, hastening its return in 1910 by over a year.

Jupiter also affected Comet Brooks 1889 V, which until 1886 had pursued its orbit in a period of 29 years. According to the calculations of S. C. Chandler it probably then passed through part of the satellite system of Jupiter without affecting the satellite motions, but was itself so perturbed as to move into a new orbit with a period of only seven years. During its appearance in 1889, and presumably as a result of its encounter with Jupiter or Jupiter's satellites, it threw off four fragments. Two of these were very faint and soon disappeared. The other two remained visible as miniature comets for some weeks. After two months these two companions also disappeared, but not before one had grown in brightness so as to surpass that of the parent comet itself.

In June, 1861, the earth passed through the tail of the great comet of that year, but at the time nothing more unusual than a faint night sky-glow was seen. The earth again passed through a comet's tail in May, 1910, when Halley's Comet made a close approach to it. The head actually passed between us and the sun, but despite a most careful search it could neither be seen nor photographed in its transit across the sun's disk. According to Andrew C. Crommelin the nucleus was probably only several feet in diameter, but other estimates put it at miles and even hundreds of miles. The head of a comet is naturally a much larger affair, and the great comet of 1811 was considered to have a head which at one stage was larger than the sun. Yet if a comet's head came into direct collision with the earth the only significant result would be a spectacular shower of meteors and perhaps a number of explosive impacts great enough to form large craters.

While "meteor" is no longer a proper term of classification for comets, it is still used as an alternative to "shooting star". Everyone has at some time looked skywards on a clear moonless night and seen a sudden streak of light popularly called a shooting star. The streak is not, of course, of stellar origin but is merely the luminous trail of a tiny piece of nickel-iron, perhaps no larger than a grain of sand. As it dashes at great speed into the upper reaches of our atmosphere frictional heat causes it to volatilize and form a brief luminous trail or "meteor train"

Meteors are generally sporadic in their appearance, and, given a clear, dark sky, can be seen at any time of the night and year. On special occasions, however, many thousands of meteors have been seen in a single hour. A shower of this nature occurred in November, 1799 when the meteors appeared to streak away from a definite point in the sky (the RADIANT) which on this occasion was in the constellation of Leo, The Lion. The Leonids, as these meteors are called, continued to appear annually in November, although in no great numbers, but in November, 1833, they again gave a great display.

It occurred to the American astronomer H. A. NEWTON,

among others, that the Leonid shower was a periodic one. He therefore examined the records of meteor showers and found that since A.D. 902 the Leonids had given great displays at intervals of 33 to 34 years. Another shower was therefore predicted for 1866, and this came up fully to expectations. However, the one for 1899 did not occur, although considerable displays took place in November, 1898, and November, 1901. The shower also failed to reach anticipated intensity in 1932.

These various features of the Leonids can be accounted for in the following ways. The fact that they appear to diverge or radiate from a definite point indicates that when they encounter the earth's atmosphere they are traveling in parallel paths. When, as with some other meteor showers, the radiant is an area instead of a definite point, this means that the paths are not strictly parallel. The diverging effect is therefore an effect of perspective, and the direction of the radiant is that of the apparent motion of the meteors relative to the earth. Before they meet the earth the meteors pursue paths around the sun, and collectively form a stream or kind of loose gravel track. If they are distributed fairly uniformly in the stream, and if the earth crosses it annually, the shower will be of about the same strength each year. But if the meteors form a fairly concentrated swarm in one part, an impressive shower will arise whenever the earth sweeps through the swarm.

The swarm which gives rise to the Leonids moves in an elongated ellipse with a period of about 33 years, and this orbit is practically identical with that of Comet Tempel, 1866 I. The swarm can be affected by planetary perturbations and it is now fairly certain that these caused the main body of Leonids to miss the earth in 1899 and 1932.

The idea that meteoric debris follows directly in the track of a comet received support after the disappearance of Comet Biela.

The earth's atmosphere.

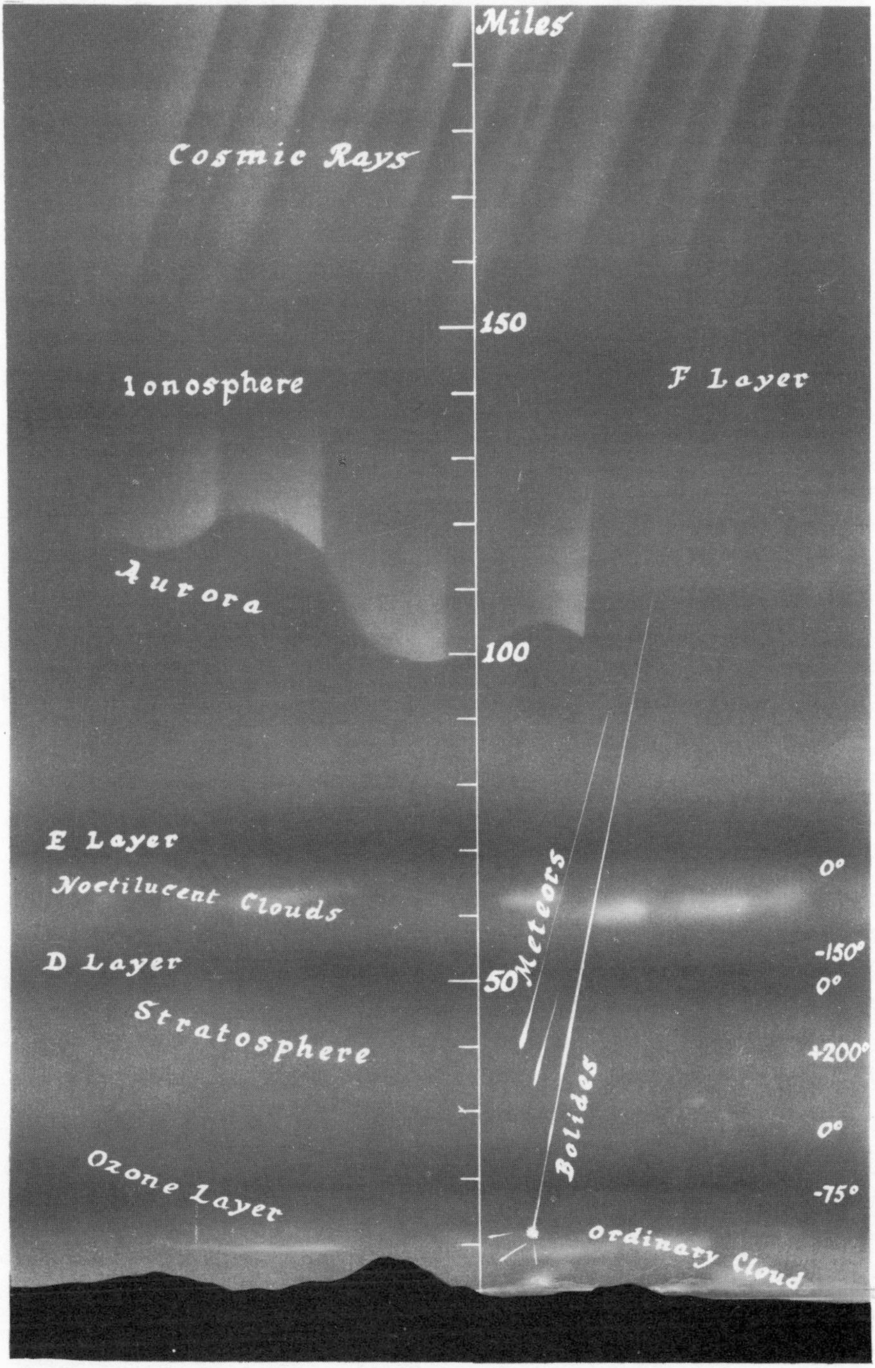
Miles
150
100
50
Cosmic Rays
Ionosphere
F Layer
Aurora
E Layer
Noctilucent Clouds
D Layer
Stratosphere
Ozone Layer
Meteors
Bolides
Ordinary Cloud
0°
-150°
0°
+200°
0°
-75°

At its return in 1845–6 the comet broke into two parts, each of which possessed its own head and tail and which traveled together for more than three months. Just before the comet was lost to sight the two parts were separated by a distance of about 160,000 miles. They reappeared in 1852, but the distance between them had increased to 1,270,000 miles. They remained visible for about three weeks and then disappeared, never to be seen again. Instead, and at about the time of Comet Biela's scheduled close approach in 1872, a splendid meteor shower was seen and its radiant point, or better, radiant area, was in the constellation of Andromeda, where it should have been if the meteors were moving along the comet's orbit. A similar shower of Andromedids occurred in 1885, an event which strengthened the view that Biela's Comet had disintegrated to form a swarm of meteors. Yet other showers of Andromedids had taken place in 1741, 1798, and 1830, that is, at times before the comet had appeared as two objects. It cannot therefore be positively asserted that the meteors once belonged to the comet or that the comet leaves a trail of meteoric material in its wake. As John G. PORTER said: *"The differences that exist between the behavior of the head of a comet and the diffuse mass of a meteor stream make it very difficult to visualize any process by which they may be transformed from one into the other."

Many meteor streams are now known, but not all of them are associated with comets or give rise to spectacular showers. The Perseids, for instance, appear regularly every August and at maximum reach about 40 to 60 meteors an hour. They appear to be fairly uniformly distributed along the orbit of Comet Swift, 1862 III. Another stream, which moves in or near the orbit of Halley's Comet, is responsible for two annual meteor showers. In early May their radiant is near the star η Aquarii, while in the third week of October it is in Orion. The greatest display given in the present century has so far been that of the October Draconids, a swarm associated with Comet Giacobini-Zinner, 1946 V. These also gave a shower in 1926 which occurred 70 days ahead of the comet, whereas that in 1946 occurred 15 days after the comet. On the first of these occasions the display arose from material in front

* Porter, J. G., *Comets and Meteor Streams*, New York, 1952, p. 68.

of the comet and not from debris following along behind. By means of radio techniques it is now possible to observe showers which take place in daytime: one of these, the Arietids of June 8, gave an hourly frequency at maximum of about 60.

The study of meteors by radar involves sending out a rapid series of intense pulses from a short-wave radio transmitter. When these pulses meet the partially-ionized gases around and behind the meteor they are reflected or echoed back to the receiver. The technique not only enables meteors to be detected in daytime or in cloudy weather but also yields information about their sizes, velocities, directions and heights, which in turn enables us to determine radiant points and orbits. Similar information can also be gathered from photographic records obtained by rapid Schmidt-type cameras designed especially for this type of work.

One significant result of studies in recent years is that the great majority of meteors move in elliptical orbits and are therefore members of the solar system. Another is that the daily number to the tenth magnitude which bombard the earth is of the order of thousands of millions, but very few escape vaporization at a height of about 50 to 100 miles. It is indeed fortunate that we live at the bottom of the ocean of air, for this acts as a protective blanket against not only harmful solar radiation but also whirling fragments from interplanetary space. As it is there is evidence that every day the earth sweeps up several thousand tons of tiny meteoric particles or MICROMETEORITES. These radiate away the frictional heat as fast as they receive it and therefore sift through the atmosphere to settle on the ground in the form of metallic dust.

When a meteor is so large that it can penetrate right through the earth's atmosphere, it is said to be a meteorite. Many thousands of these are preserved in museums and altogether weigh about 500 tons, but millions more await discovery. They may be roughly divided into three classes. Some consist largely of iron alloyed with nickel and sometimes with other metals. These can be cut, polished and etched with dilute acid to reveal a peculiar crystalline structure called the WIDMANSTÄTTEN FIGURE. Others are a mixture of nickel-iron and stone, while the third group is basically stony, consisting essentially of silicate minerals with

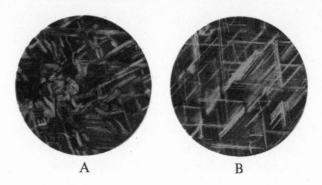

A.   Crystalline structure in two different meteorites.
B.   Enlarged section.

small amounts of metallic alloys. No chemical element has been found amongst them which is not known on earth.

Sometimes a large stony meteorite bursts asunder in its flight through the atmosphere. It does so with a deafening sound and scatters fragments over a large area. There are several records of quite heavy showers of stones. One occurred on April 26, 1803, when a large fiery mass sped across the daytime sky and then exploded. Thousands of hot stones were scattered far and wide around the town of L'Aigle in Normandy. Some of them were examined by the French physicist Jean-Baptiste BIOT, who also compared eye-witness accounts and concluded that the main mass came from the interplanetary space. This was a novel idea at the time, despite the fact that Ernst CHLADNI of Germany had in 1794 suggested that fire-balls and falling stones were of celestial origin and were heated by friction with the atmosphere. Another large fall of stones occurred on February 3, 1882, at Moos, Hungary, and on July 19, 1912, a shower of about 14,000 stones fell in Arizona.

Reference has already been made to the Barringer and other large craters formed as a result of meteoric impact. These appear to have been formed many thousands of years ago, and we have necessarily to *infer* their meteoric origin. On June 30, 1908, however, a great fireball was seen on its course over central Siberia. It crashed in an isolated region, felling a forest of trees and creating an air wave which was registered in England and a ground wave which affected all the SEISMOGRAPHS in Europe. A similar fall occurred in eastern Siberia on February 12, 1947. Once again the fireball was seen by many people: it was so bright that it temporarily blinded the eyes of those who watched it, and cast moving shadows. Some minutes after it disappeared powerful detonations were heard. An expedition sent later to examine the area of impact found evidence that the meteorite had exploded above ground and scattered fragments over an area of about a square mile. The expedition located 122 craters which ranged in diameter from about 1½ to 90 feet. It also collected about 23 tons of meteoric material, and made a thorough survey of the nature and distribution of large quantities of meteoric particles and dust.

The largest known meteorite called Hoba West, still lies where it fell near Grootfontein in south-west Africa. It is roughly rectangular in shape and weighs about 60 tons. The largest preserved meteorite is AHNIGHITO, brought by Peary from Greenland in 1897 and now in the American Museum-Hayden Planetarium, New York City. When weighed in 1956, Ahnighito just turned the scales at 34 tons.

The Barringer meteor crater, Arizona.

Until manned space-flight to the moon and planets becomes a reality, meteorites will remain the only celestial bodies which we can examine in the same way as terrestrial substances. They have therefore been subjected to a number of laboratory tests, one of which is particularly interesting since it gives some idea of their age. This method takes advantage of the fact that meteorites contain very small amounts of uranium, thorium and helium. These elements can be regarded as links in a chain of RADIO-ACTIVE DECAY, and their present relative abundance serves as a measure of the extent of this decay. The "age" arrived at in this way is presumably the time which has elapsed since the meteorite solidified, and is found to range from a few million years to several thousand million years. As at present determined the age, or rather, ages, of meteorites have a range similar to that of the earth's oldest rocks.

Right. A tektite, or small glass-like object found in various parts of the earth and believed to have fallen from interplanetary space.

A meteorite, showing signs of surface fusion.

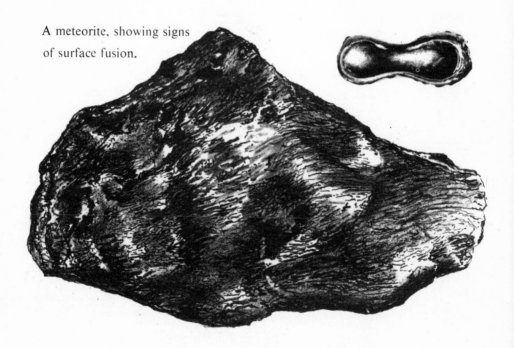

7. The stars

Anyone who observes the sky free from the glare of city lights and on a clear, moonless night, may feel that the number of stars he can see is limitless. Yet an actual count will reveal that this is by no means the case. The keenest vision will detect at any one time no more than some two thousand to three thousand stars. These range from the brightest, or first magnitude stars of the Greeks, to the just discernible stars of about the sixth magnitude. Even if the count is extended to include the stars of the entire heavens from pole to pole the total number will be no more than about 6000 to 7000.

These numbers may appear surprisingly small, but in the days before photography they were large enough to make the successful cataloguing and charting of the stars a difficult task. Yet early workers in this field may have been encouraged by the fact that the stars appeared to maintain the same relative positions among themselves, an appearance which led to the idea that the starry heavens is a vast complex of *fixed* stars. It was thought that once a star atlas had been formed it would be valid for all time, and could serve as a permanent reference system against which one could plot the movements of the sun, moon, planets and comets. "It is upon the observation of the fixed stars as upon immovable pillars," wrote John KEILL in the early eighteenth century, "that the whole science of astronomy is erected, and by them it is sustained." But in practice things turned out quite differently. The grid-reference system of right ascension and declination, based on the FIRST POINT OF ARIES, was a *moving* framework, and star positions are exact relative to it only at a specific time or epoch. Again, the introduction and development of new instruments and observing techniques enabled astronomers to determine star positions with ever-increasing accuracy. Where the early observers did well to obtain an accuracy of about one minute of arc, early telescopic observations could provide star positions correct to within a few seconds of arc. Then came the discovery which grew into the general concept that the stars, as suns, are *moving* suns, and that the sun, as a star, is a *moving* star.

After the ancient *Almagest* of Ptolemy, the first modern star atlas of general value was the *Uranometria* published in 1603 by Johann BAYER of Augsburg. In this the principal stars are designated by the letters of the Greek alphabet with the brightest star in each constellation being α, the next brightest β, and so on. Hence Regulus, the brightest star in Leo, The Lion, is also called

Stellar parallax. Comparatively nearby stars are photographed against the background of very distant stars at six-monthly intervals, that is from opposite sides of the earth's orbit. The apparent shift in position of the nearer star is equal to the angular diameter of the earth's orbit as measured from the star itself. Since the diameter of the earth's orbit is known the distance of the star can be easily calculated.

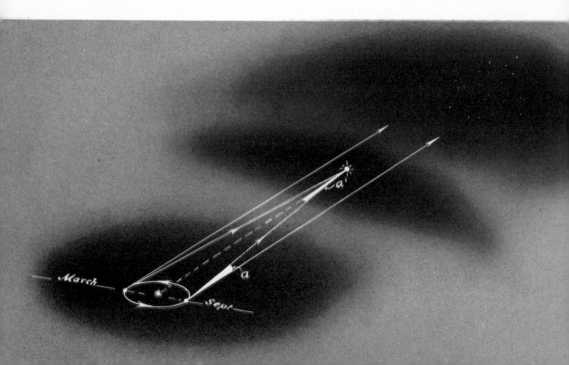

α Leonis. Denebola, the second brightest star in Leo, is β Leonis, the third brightest is γ Leonis. Unfortunately this arrangement was not followed rigorously, and the stars in The Big Dipper, for example, are lettered not according to brightness but in the order of their positions. Astronomers still retain Bayer's suffixes and the order in which he arranged them, but for the fainter stars visible to the unaided eye they use the star numbers assigned by John FLAMSTEED. During his work as first Astronomer Royal at the Royal Observatory, Greenwich, Flamsteed formed a larger atlas of about 3000 stars which he numbered according to the constellations. Hence among the fainter naked-eye stars of Leo we find stars called 23 Leonis and 61 Leonis, but as far as their postiions are concerned, all down to the very faintest are described in terms of right ascension and declination.

Astronomers also continue to use the range of six magnitudes introduced by Hipparchus, but have arranged it so that a star of the first magnitude is exactly 100 times brighter than one of the sixth magnitude. The brightness ratio for one magnitude is therefore 2·512 or $\sqrt[5]{100}$, so that a star of the first magnitude is 2·512 times brighter than one of the second magnitude, which in turn is 2·512 times brighter than one of the third magnitude . . . and so on. The scale has been extended to embrace, at one extreme, stars of the 22nd and 23rd magnitudes, and at the other, stars and objects brighter than the first magnitude. The sun, for example, has a magnitude of −27·72; Sirius, the next brightest star, is of magnitude −1·6 and Canopus, the third brightest, is of magnitude −0·86.

The apparent visual brightness of a star depends on several factors, but two of the most important are its distance and its actual brightness, or LUMINOSITY. As long as the sun appears as a disk its surface will appear to be of the same apparent brightness regardless of its distance from the observer. But if we move so far away from the sun that it ceases to present a disk and looks like an ordinary star, its brightness will vary inversely as the square of the distance. This means that when we double, triple and quadruple our distance from the sun its brightness will decrease to a quarter, a ninth, and a sixteenth respectively of its former value.

The apparent brightness of stars decreases in accordance with this INVERSE SQUARE LAW OF ILLUMINATION. Two stars which appear to be of the same brightness are not necessarily at the same distance from us. One of them could, for instance, be four times as luminous and yet twice as distant as the other, or nine times as luminous and three times as distant. The stars are certainly suns distributed in depth in space, but they are suns differing widely among themselves in luminosity.

Once the distance and brightness of a star are known, we can derive its luminosity by applying the inverse square law of illumination. The main difficulty in this procedure lies in estimating the distances of even the nearest stars with anything like reasonable accuracy. One of the ways of tackling the problem is to use a trigonometrical method based on surveying principles. As the earth moves around the sun it is, at intervals of six months, at the ends of a baseline whose length is two astronomical units, or nearly 186,000,000 miles. As seen from each end of this baseline a comparatively near star will appear to be displaced relative to the background of very faint and probably more distant stars. One half of the angle of displacement is known as the star's parallax. Not until 1838 were observations of sufficient accuracy made to establish and give a convincing estimation of this parallax. The star concerned was 61 Cygni, whose parallax as measured by the German astronomer F. W. Bessel showed that it was about half a million times further away from us than is the sun.

The nearest known star, and therefore the star with the largest parallax, is Proxima Centauri, an eleventh magnitude star situated near to and physically connected with the bright southern star α Centauri. Its parallax, 0·76″, is therefore the angle which the radius of the earth's orbit would subtend at the star's distance of about 25,000 billion miles. Perhaps a better idea of the smallness of this angle is obtained if we represent the earth's annual path around the sun by a circle one inch in diameter. The star would then be represented by a point of light four miles away. If two lines are drawn from the light to the ends of a diameter of the circle, the angle between these lines is what has to be measured in order to find twice the parallax and hence the distance of the star.

By another illustration, due to Edward PICKERING, the problem of determining the apparent parallax displacement of 61 Cygni is like measuring the height of a man two hundred miles away.

Because the distances of the stars are so great, astronomers use units of distance which are much greater than the mile. One of these is the LIGHT-YEAR, or distance which light would travel in a year, and this is equal to about 6000 billion miles. The distance of the sun is just over eight light-minutes, but that of Proxima Centauri is 4·28 light-years. When we look at Proxima Centauri we therefore see it not as it is but as it was 4·28 years ago. Another convenient unit is the PARSEC, equivalent to 3·26 light-years. At this distance a star has a parallax of 1″ or arc, while at 10 parsecs its parallax is 0·1″, etc.

The work of estimating star distances by trigonometrical parallaxes is now done by taking photographs of the selected stars at half-year intervals and then measuring the tiny displacements upon the plates. About 6000 stars have had their distances estimated in this way, but only some 600 of them are less than 65 light-years distant. Among the 600 are many of the brightest stars which range in distance from 4·3 light-years to over 600 light-years from us. Yet more surprising is their vastly greater range in luminosity. Sirius, the brightest, is 8·7 light-years distant and has an apparent visual magnitude of −1·6; we therefore find that its luminosity must be 23 times that of the sun. The star α Centauri, 4·3 light-years away and hence about half the distance of Sirius, has an apparent magnitude of 0·3 and a luminosity equal to that of the sun. Rigel, or β Orionis, also has an apparent magnitude of 0·3, but because of its great distance of 850 light-years it must have a luminosity at least 23,000 times that of the sun. At the other end of the magnitude scale, and within a radius of 16 light-years from the sun, we find many stars which are below naked-eye visibility. Among them are Proxima Centauri, Barnard's Star (apparent magnitude 9·46), and Wolf 359 (apparent magnitude 13·5), all with luminosities far less than that of the sun.

To compare stellar luminosities, astronomers imagine that the stars are all at one and the same distance. They then compute how bright the stars would appear if seen from that distance. For con-

venience the distance chosen is ten parsecs, and the apparent magnitude which a star would have there is called its ABSOLUTE
MAGNITUDE. On this basis the absolute magnitude of Rigel is
minus 6·2; of the sun, 4·9 and of Wolf 359, 16·5. Thus Rigel
is about 23,000 times more luminous than the sun, and the sun is
about 23,000 times more luminous than Wolf 359. Differences so
immense compel us to examine the stars in greater detail – to
consider their sizes, temperatures, and physical constitutions.

From ordinary experience we find that if we increase the temperature of a metal bar or rod the metal undergoes changes in
color. At first it glows with a deep reddish hue and brightens as
the color changes from deep red to cherry red and then to orange
and yellow. At even higher temperatures the color changes imper-
ceptibly from yellow to white and finally approximates to bluish-
white. As similar hues are noticed visually among the stars, we
may infer that the differences in color are brought about by

To define the relative aspect of the components of a double star the astronomer
sometimes uses a micrometer eyepiece. With this he can measure the angular
separation between them and also the positron angle (p.a.) or angle which a
line joining them makes with the N.S. line (and measured in the sense indicated).

differences in temperature. Hence white Sirius and Rigel must be hotter than orange Aldebaran and Arcturus which, in turn, must be hotter than reddish Betelgeuse and Antares.

That this inference is correct is amply borne out by the results of stellar spectrography. Although the spectra of the stars differ widely in appearance, they can in the main be grouped into seven classes. These classes form a continuous sequence denoted by the arbitrary letters O, B, A, F, G, K, M and have each been divided into ten sub-divisions by affixing a number from 0 to 9 to each letter. The sun, of spectral type Go, is therefore fairly well down the sequence.

The main features of each class in the sequence are as follows:

Class	*Spectrum*
O	There are comparatively few absorption lines. Those present arise from highly ionized atoms of helium, silicon, nitrogen; hydrogen lines are weak.
B	The hydrogen lines are stronger and are accompanied by lines due to neutral helium and ionized magnesium, ionized oxygen and ionized silicon.
A	The hydrogen lines are strong and broad, while the lines due to helium and ionized oxygen are absent. In this class lines of the ionized metals iron, titanium and calcium appear.
F	The H and K lines of ionized calcium are the most prominent, then those of hydrogen, which are weaker than in Class A. As the lines of ionized iron, titanium and calcium strengthen, those of hydrogen weaken.
G	The H and K lines of calcium continue to strengthen, while those of hydrogen weaken. The lines of neutral metals increase in prominence, and the molecular bands of cyanogen and hydro-carbon begin to appear.
K	The H and K lines of ionized calcium are at their strongest. Lines due to neutral metals are prominent, and the molecular bands which appeared in class G are stronger.
M	The calcium lines are still prominent, as also are the molecular bands or flutings, especially those due to titanium oxide. These bands cover large portions of the green and blue parts of the continuous background.

In the early years of astrophysics it was thought that these differences arose because of variations in the chemical composition of stellar atmospheres. It is now well established that the sequence O to M corresponds to a sequence of decreasing temperature and not to any scarcity or abundance of a particular element. Thus O-type stars have surface temperatures upwards of 25,000° centigrade; the sun, of spectral type G, has a surface temperature of about 6000° centigrade; M-type stars have surface temperatures of 3500° centigrade. As far as color is concerned, O-type stars are bluish-white, G-type are yellowish, and M-type are reddish. In brief, the range from spectral types O to M corresponds to a color range from bluish-white to red and a temperature range from about 25,000° centigrade to 3000° centigrade.

The above outline of the spectral sequence suggests that it is a comparatively simple matter to assign a star to its appropriate place in the sequence. This is far from the truth. Stellar spectra can certainly be grouped according to certain broad features, but those so placed in any one class or even class subdivision can differ considerably in detail. This feature will be made clearer in subsequent pages. In some cases a star could not be assigned to any place in the sequence, and it became necessary to precede class O with an additional class W and to add classes S, R, and N at the bottom of the sequence. The classes, moreover, merge one into the other, and there is but little difference in the main spectral features of, say, a G9 star and one in class K0.

Until 1889 astronomers knew only of visual binaries – of pairs of stars which revolved around their common center of gravity and which could be seen as two stars through the telescope. Sir William Herschel had opened up this fascinating field by discovering many hundreds of double stars, but comparatively few of them had been found to be physically connected, that is, to be binaries. Most of them appeared to be double only because they happened to be almost in the same line of sight: one of the two stars was far beyond the other and had no physical connection with it. Double stars of this kind are called OPTICAL DOUBLES. To sort out the binaries from the optical doubles it was necessary to look for changes in the direction of the line joining the two stars and the angular distance between them. This involved making careful micrometrical measurements over a long period, for the two stars generally moved around each other in periods of tens and even hundreds of years. But once the mean separation and distance of the system are known the actual distance between the two stars can be readily found. If the period has also been determined, it is possible to apply Kepler's Third Law and thence to find the sum of the masses of the two stars. The relative masses of the two stars can also be found, but this requires knowledge of the apparent relative orbit of the smaller or secondary star about the primary and then a computation of the true relative orbit.

In 1889 the Doppler-Fizeau velocity shift in spectra, described in Chapter 2, led E. C. Pickering to discover the first SPECTRO-SCOPIC BINARY. In this type of double star the two components are so close together that they cannot be resolved by direct observation. The first of them to be discovered was Mizar, or ζ Ursae Majoris, a star in the handle of the Big Dipper. Pickering found that at regular intervals the lines of its spectrum appeared double

A binary system. Two stars with masses in the ratio 3:1 orbit around a single point F, the center of gravity of the system. The orbits are ellipses and the position of the stars at any time is such that they could be connected by a line passing through F, and their distances from F will always be in the ratio 1:3. Two positions are shown.

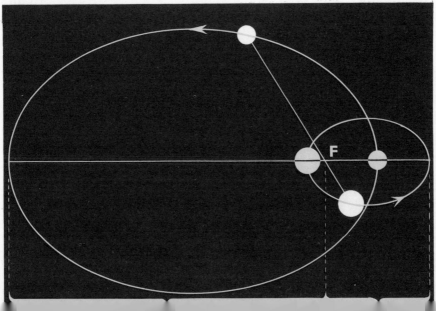

The Doppler-Fizeau effect, produced by wave motion plus or minus observer motion. An observer on the stationary buoy can measure the "true" number of waves per second (the frequency). Observers on the two ships get modified impressions of the wave frequency owing to motion in the "line of sight". Those on the left ship receive a reduced number of waves per second, corresponding in optical work to a red shift. Those on the right ship receive an increased number of waves per second corresponding in optical work to a blue shift.

and then single. He interpreted this change as a Doppler-Fizeau effect brought about by two stars similar in luminosity and spectral type which revolve around their common center of gravity in a period of about 20·5 days.

The doubling effect cannot be seen when the two stars move across the line-of-sight, for then there is no motion towards or away from the observer. When the orbits are practically edge-on, however, one star will eclipse or partially eclipse the other. Binaries which do this undergo light variations and are called eclipsing variables. One of the most striking of these is Algol, or β Persei: the line-shifts in its spectrum keep pace with the light

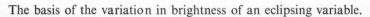

The basis of the variation in brightness of an eclipsing variable.

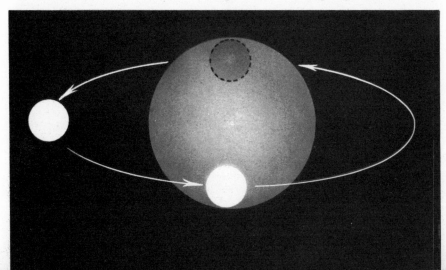

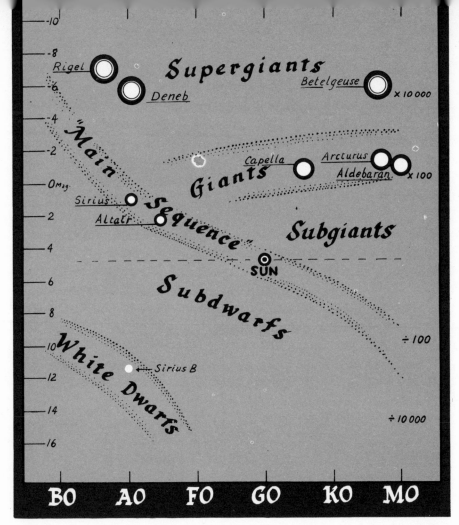

The main features of the H-R or Hertzsprung Russell Diagram, based on a sample of stars limited only by their apparent magnitude.

variation and the latter has characteristics which could only arise if one star is being regularly eclipsed by another.

The study of double stars in general and eclipsing variables in particular has yielded a wealth of data on the sizes, shapes, masses, temperatures and internal structure of the component stars. These findings supplement others which show that the stars have a great range not only in luminosity but also in density.

A good way of obtaining a general picture of the wide variety of stars is to arrange them according to spectral class and absolute visual magnitude. This, as the reader will appreciate, is similar to arranging them according to temperature and luminosity. The diagram obtained in this way is known as the HERTZSPRUNG-RUSSELL or H–R DIAGRAM. It shows that the great bulk of stars lies in a band which runs diagonally downwards from left to right. This band is referred to as the main sequence, and the luminosity of the stars in it falls off rapidly with decreasing temperature. The sun, a member of this main sequence, is in luminosity, size, mass and density a fairly average star.

Above the main sequence we find a group of stars with luminosities far greater than their spectral counterparts in the main sequence. These are the giants and SUPERGIANTS – their immense sizes giving them correspondingly large surface areas through which to pour out their radiation. Below and to the left of the main sequence are the WHITE DWARFS, or stars which are extremely hot, dense, and far smaller than the sun.

The following table enables us to compare various stars typical of their group in the H–R diagram.

Star	Luminosity; sun = I	Surface temperature; °C.	Radius; sun = I	Mass	Density; sun = I
MAIN SEQUENCE					
Barnard's star	0·0004	3100	0·16	0·18	45
α Centauri A	1·0	6000	1·0	1·23	1·23
Altair	8·3	8600	1·4	1·7	0·6
Sirius A	23	11,200	1·8	2·35	0·42
Procyon A	6	6500	1·9	1·7	0·16
Vega	48	11,200	2·4	3·0	0·11
β Centauri	1300	21,000	11	25	0·018
GIANTS					
Arcturus	76	4100	30	8	0·0003
Aldebaran	120	3300	60	4	0·00002
β Pegasi	170	2900	170	9	0·000002
SUPERGIANTS					
Betelgeuse	13,000	3100	300	15	0·0000006
Antares	700	3100	285	30	0·0000003
WHITE DWARFS					
Sirius B	0·008	7500	0·022	0·99	27,000
van Maanen's Star	0·00016	7500	0·007	0·14	400,000

It is at once apparent from even this small selection that the stars have a small range in mass but a remarkably wide range in volume and density. At the one end of the scale are supergiants like Betelgeuse and Antares which are stars of high luminosity but comparatively low surface temperature. These must therefore be enormously expanded spheres of highly diffuse gas. The white dwarfs, on the other hand, are small stars of low luminosity; they are so compact that their material is several thousand times as dense as that of the sun. As far as the main sequence stars are concerned, the stars of greater mass are those of greater luminosity and vice versa. This important relationship, discovered by Sir Arthur EDDINGTON in 1924, is called the MASS-LUMINOSITY LAW. Once astronomers have a good estimate of a star's luminosity they can straightway work out its mass. Alternatively, if the masses of the components of a double or multiple system of stars are known, application of the Mass-luminosity Law yields their individual luminosities.

The reality of giant and dwarf stars does not rest solely on the study of eclipsing variables. In 1914 Walter ADAMS and Arnold KOHLSCHÜTTER discovered differences between otherwise similar spectra which made it possible to decide whether a star was a giant or a main sequence dwarf. Certain spectral lines are stronger in giants and certain other lines are stronger in dwarfs. Adams also found that a number of stars of the same spectral type could be placed in order of luminosity by the relative strengths of pairs of lines in their almost identical spectra. Using this technique he began to determine the luminosities of various stars, then, by using their apparent magnitudes, he could estimate their distances or find SPECTROSCOPIC PARALLAXES. Of the several thousand stars whose distances have been estimated in this way, most are beyond the range of trigonometrical parallaxes. Furthermore, several stars large enough and near enough have had their diameters measured by a special optical method introduced by Albert MICHELSON and called the STELLAR INTERFEROMETER. It was first tried out in 1920 on the 100-inch Mount Wilson reflector and enabled Francis G. PEASE to measure the angular diameter of Betelgeuse. Other low-temperature giant and supergiant stars have had their diameters measured by this method and the results obtained are in good agreement with the predicted values. The largest observed angular diameter, for o Ceti or Mira Ceti, was only 0·056′. Combined with the star's distance of about 250 light-years, this gives a diameter of nearly 400,000,000 miles. If the sun could be placed at the centre of Mira Ceti, the star would easily contain the orbit of the planet Mars.

The densities assigned to the stars, are, of course, average densities. There is every reason to believe that the density of stellar material increases rapidly towards the center of a star. Similarly the temperatures listed are those of a star's surface or atmosphere and are far lower than those which must exist deep in its interior. Yet at the center of a star, where the pressure and density are enormous and where the temperature can run into millions and tens of millions of degrees, the material still retains the properties of a gas.

The particular conditions and high temperatures which must exist in stellar interiors are strong pointers to the most likely source of stellar energy. According to the most favored theory, first proposed by Robert d'E. Atkinson and Houtermans in 1929, and later developed by Hans Bethe and C. F. von Weissäcker, the stars derive their energy from a process which involves a cycle of THERMONUCLEAR REACTIONS. There are two chief reactions: the HYDROGEN CHAIN or PROTON-PROTON REACTION, and the CARBON CYCLE. In the first, hydrogen nuclei or protons are converted into helium nuclei, in the second, carbon nuclei act as CATALYSTS and hydrogen is again converted into helium. Both transformations are accompanied by the simultaneous conversion of mass into energy. This energy slowly leaks out to the star's surface and then streams out in the form of radiation. In general the proton-proton reaction appears to play a predominant role in stars at the lower end of the main sequence. As we move up the sequence towards the massive, high-temperature B-type stars, the carbon-cycle becomes increasingly important.

At present the sun pours out its substance at the rate of over 4,000,000 tons a second, yet so great is its store of hydrogen that even at this fantastic rate it would diminish in mass by only one-tenth of one per cent in 15 billion years. Even when the supply of hydrogen is exhausted, the sun could still continue to shine. It would contract, and in so doing might well produce an increase in

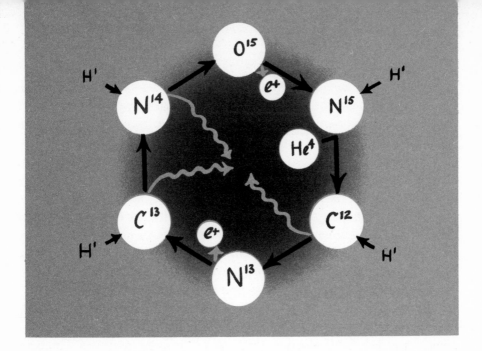

The carbon-nitrogen cycle. A carbon nucleus (C^{12}) captures a hydrogen nucleus (H^1) and changes into a nitrogen nucleus (N^{13}). The N^{13} nucleus emits a positron ($e+$) and changes into a carbon isotope (C^{13}). The C^{13} captures another H^1 and becomes a nitrogen isotope (N^{14}). This captures an H^1 and becomes an oxygen nucleus (O^{15}). The oxygen nucleus emits a positron and becomes another nitrogen isotope N^{15}. This captures an H^1 and changes into the carbon isotope C^{12} which started the cycle, plus a helium nucleus He^4. Hence during the cycle four hydrogen atoms are captured, one helium atom and two positrons liberated, and the original carbon atom restored to start the next cycle.

temperature great enough to initiate thermonuclear reactions in helium. If the helium in turn became exhausted, the sun would contract still further and might increase in central temperature to about 600,000,000 degrees, when a carbon reaction could take place, and so on. While the vast majority of stars seem to be transforming hydrogen into helium, a few appear to have already reached the later helium and carbon stages.

Another outcome from the close scrutiny of stellar spectra was the measurement, by Sir William HUGGINS in 1868, of the line-of-sight velocity or RADIAL VELOCITY of a star. Using a powerful spectroscope, Huggins found that the lines in the spectrum of Sirius were shifted slightly towards the red. He recognized this as a definite Doppler-Fizeau effect, and after making allowance for the earth's motion, suggested that Sirius had a speed of recession from the sun of 29·4 miles a second. Further measurements in 1872 yielded a lower velocity of about 20 miles a second, a close approximation to the modern value.

Huggins also obtained a series of results for other stars, but the line shifts were really far too minute to be measured with accuracy by visual methods. The work is now done photographically, that is, with the spectrograph, but even so it would be truer to say that the radial velocities are estimated rather than determined. Estimates of radial velocities for several thousand stars show that the majority range from about five to 25 miles a second, with some stars approaching and some receding from the sun.

Since spectrography gives information about velocities directly towards or away from the sun, it is natural to ask whether there exists any way of finding a star's actual motion in space. This can indeed be done, but with the requirement that one must also take into account the TANGENTIAL VELOCITY, or velocity across the line of sight. Because of its tangential velocity, a nearby star appears to move slowly against the background of more distant stars. The amount of the angular movement, usually expressed in seconds of arc per year or per century, is called the star's PROPER MOTION. It was first detected in 1718 by Halley, who found that since the time of Ptolemy the stars Sirius, Aldebaran and Arcturus had changed their positions relative to the other stars. As might be expected, the larger the angular proper motion of a star, the greater are the chances of its being comparatively near. It was on this consideration that Bessel fixed on 61 Cygni when he wished to try out the method of trigonometrical parallaxes. He knew that the star had a large proper motion – the largest known at the time, amounting to five seconds of arc a year – and judged it to be nearer than all the rest. At this rate 61 Cygni can cover an angular distance equal to the apparent width of the moon in about 380 years. The star with the largest proper motion, 10·3″ a year, is one discovered by Edward BARNARD in 1916 and appropriately called "Barnard's Runaway Star". This, however, is an exceptional case, and for most stars the proper motion is extremely small.

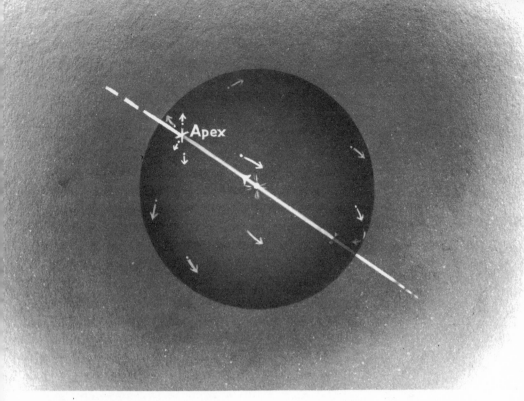

The effect of the sun's motion in space is to cause the stars to appear to move away from the solar apex, or point on the celestial sphere to which the solar motion is directed.

The study of proper motions reveals the interesting fact that the sun, like other stars, is a moving star. This feature was discovered by W. Herschel who examined the proper motions of 27 stars and found that they reflected the sun's own movement through space. Because of this movement the stars appear to be moving away from a particular point located in the constellation of Hercules and called the SOLAR APEX. For the same reason they appear to be closing in on the ANTAPEX or point directly opposite. Herschel had no way of determining the speed of the sun's motion, for nothing was then known of the Doppler-Fizeau effect and the spectroscope had yet to be invented. Early in the present century, however, William CAMPBELL and J. H. Moore of the Lick Observatory investigated the radial velocities of 2149 stars and found that the sun's speed is about 12 miles a second. This must therefore be allowed for when astronomers wish to study the motions of the stars among themselves.

8. Interesting stars and star clusters

In the preceding discussion of proper motions we have assumed that the stars move in space in constant directions during the comparatively short time over which their positions have been accurately observed. This is not strictly true, for as early as 1834 Bessel had begun to suspect that the bright star Sirius, sometimes called the Dog Star, did not pursue a straight path against the background of faint and distant stars. Ten years later, and after a careful study of the star's proper motion, Bessel was able to assert that Sirius moves with non-uniform motion in a sinuous path which is repeated at intervals of about fifty years. The reason for this he declared, lies in the fact that Sirius has a companion too faint to be seen but sufficiently massive to swing the bright star about a common center of gravity.

The very faint companion inferred by Bessel was first seen by Alvan G. Clark in 1862 while he was testing a refracting telescope of $18\frac{1}{2}$ inches aperture. The two stars were thereafter studied as a binary system with a view to finding the relative paths, and from them, the true orbits. The brighter star is now designated Sirius A and the fainter star Sirius B, although the latter is sometimes referred to as The Companion of Sirius or merely as The Pup. Their physical characteristics have already been given, but we reproduce them here to facilitate comparison.

Star	Luminosity; sun = 1	Surface temperature; °C	Radius; sun = 1	Ma⸴	Density; sun = 1
Sirius A	23	11,200	1·8	2·4	0·42
Sirius B	0·008	7500	0·022	0·99	27,000

The fact that Sirius B is no feebly radiating red star, but an intensely hot one was first found in 1915 by W. S. Adams of Mount Wilson Observatory. Despite difficulties due to the interfering glare of Sirius A, Adams succeeded in obtaining spectrograms of The Companion which revealed it to be white, of spectral type A5, and high surface temperature. Yet while its surface temperature is greater than the sun's, its luminosity is less than a hundredth of that of the sun. This can mean only that despite its large mass the star has a surface area so small as to make it a body of planetary dimensions. Small wonder, therefore, that the average density of its material turns out to be 40,000 times greater than that of water. At this density a cubic inch would weigh nearly a ton.

At first, and because of its small size and high density, Sirius B was regarded as a particularly rare type of star. W. J. Luyten of the University of Minnesota has since discovered about a hundred white dwarfs, several of which are companions to other stars. In all probability they are quite numerous, but those beyond the sun's immediate vicinity escape detection because of their extreme faintness. Those associated with other stars have had their masses and sizes estimated and have been found to possess extremely high average densities. One white dwarf, known as van Manaan's Star, has an average density ten times that of Sirius B. In size they appear to range from the planet Mercury to the planet Venus.

It is now suggested that a white dwarf was once a massive main sequence star which used up almost all of its available store of hydrogen. Unable to maintain the hydrogen-to-helium thermonuclear reaction and the necessary high internal temperature, it collapsed under its own gravitational contraction, and in so doing increased considerably in density. As a white dwarf it is regarded as being in a "degenerate state" in the sense that the atomic nuclei and electrons deep in the interior are so tightly packed together

that they have lost their individuality as atoms and cease to be-
have as in an ordinary gas.

While even the nearest white dwarfs appear only as very faint
stars, the same cannot be said of the red giants and supergiants.
Two of them, Betelgeuse (magnitude 0·9) and Antares (magnitude
1·2) are among the brightest stars in the night sky and many
others are well above naked-eye visibility. Owing to the smallness
of its parallax (of the order of only 0·005″), the distance of Betelgeuse is not accurately known. It probably lies between 600 and
700 light-years, and this uncertainty means that there is a corresponding uncertainty as to its size.

As we have seen, Betelgeuse is one of the few stars whose
angular diameter has been measured with the stellar interfero-

The supergiant Betelgeuse compared in size with the orbits of earth and Mars.

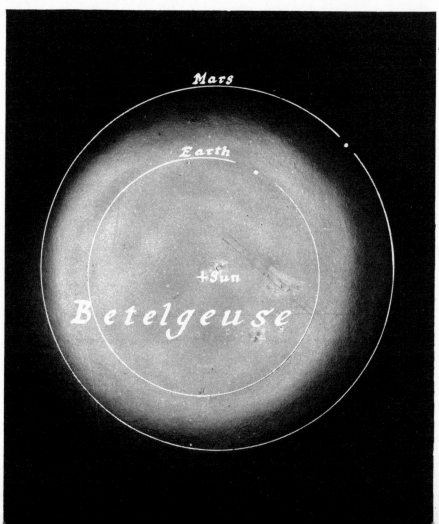

meter, and if we take the mean of the parallax determinations, the linear diameter comes out at about 300,000,000 miles. This again is not strictly correct, for Betelgeuse PULSATES, or waxes and wanes in size. Proof of this is provided by the interferometer, which shows that the diameter varies from between 300 and 420 solar diameters. The star also brightens as it waxes in size and fades as it wanes, but the change hardly exceeds a magnitude, from 0·4 to 1·4. In period the light variation is semi-regular, with main fluctuations once every 140 to 300 days. Several other giant M-type stars are semi-regular variables, but it is not known for sure whether they are all pulsating stars. There are also large numbers of red and reddish stars whose brightness varies in a semi-regular and irregular manner, but for the vast majority the variation involves a change of several magnitudes over long intervals of time.

Since Betelgeuse is of spectral type M2 and temperature 3100° centigrade, its maximum energy intensity is not in the blue and violet parts of the spectrum but in the red, and far red. It therefore appears at a disadvantage when compared visually with bluish-white Rigel in the same constellation. Yet when we consider the total radiation emitted by each of the two stars in turn, Betelgeuse has by far the greater output. If our eyes were visually sensitive to all the radiation received from Betelgeuse, it would appear almost as bright as Sirius.

Antares, or α Scorpii, appears to be about as massive as Betelgeuse and to have a diameter of 250,000,000 miles. Both stars have average densities so low that they are of the order of one-millionth of the density of our atmosphere at ground level. Even larger in size is ε Aurigae, a fairly bright star at the apex of a small triangle known as The Kids. This is an ECLIPSING BINARY with an exceptionally long period of 27 years, and as the brighter F-type component star moves around the M-type primary it is partially eclipsed for about two years. Its light during this time is never completely cut off but passes through the extremely tenuous atmosphere of the primary. The latter has a diameter estimated to be 2700 times that of the sun, and a visual luminosity so low that at its great distance of about 3000 light years it is invisible.

Another remarkable M-type supergiant is o Ceti, or Mira Ceti, a star characteristic of the great majority of long-period variables whose rise to light-maximum is more rapid than their fall to light-minimum. When discovered by David FABRICIUS in 1596 it appeared of the third magnitude, but after two months had fallen into invisibility and was not seen again until 1637. The period is now known to average 330 days, during which time the star can range from a maximum magnitude between two and five and to a minimum magnitude between eight and 10. These differences are in part accounted for by supposing that the star is accompanied by a faint companion which is itself variable, but the main change appears to be due to its own change in size. Mira Ceti can be imagined as a great pulsating gas sphere, distant about 250 light-years and having a mean diameter 460 times that of the sun.

Coupled with the light variation are significant changes in spectrum. Upon the continuous background are numerous absorption lines and bands due to chemical compounds, those of titanium oxide being particularly prominent. Superimposed on this absorption spectrum are bright lines which vary in brightness with different phases of the light-variation. As the star fades the absorption bands increase in intensity at different stages of the light curve. These changes are in the main ascribed to a fall in surface temperature; it is estimated that while this is around 3000° centigrade at maximum it drops to as low as 1700° centigrade at minimum.

Another conspicuous variable star is β Persei, or Algol, the classic representative of the eclipsing variables. Discovered by Geminiano Montanari in 1667, its variability was first fully investigated by John GOODRICKE in 1782. Since then the star has gone through its brightness variations with great regularity. For about $2\frac{1}{2}$ days it appears to be almost constant in brightness with a magnitude of 2·3. Then for five hours it fades to one-fourth of this brightness and after another five hours regains its former maximum brilliance.

Goodricke realized that this light variation could best be described by supposing that Algol has a "dark" companion. As this less luminous star passes nearly in front of the primary the latter undergoes partial eclipse. Goodricke's hypothesis has been fully confirmed by spectrographic observation, and the "dark" companion is now known to be slightly larger than the brighter star. In addition, a more detailed study of the light variations reveals a small secondary minimum and changes which show not only that the companion star is itself faintly luminous but also that it reflects the light of the primary. Recent observations have also revealed that the two stars are in orbital motion relative to a third star and suggest that there may be even a fourth star, a white dwarf with an orbital period of about 188 years.

In 1784 Goodricke discovered the variability of β Lyrae, another interesting eclipsing binary. Its light curve has two unequal minima separated by equal maxima and is characterized by a continuous light variation. In this case the period is nearly 13 days and the maximum light range is about three magnitudes. The system consists of two unequally bright stars so close together that they are almost in contact. In this circumstance they distort each other tidally and therefore have elongated shapes that are highly spheroidal or even ellipsoidal. In other systems, and where the two components are very close together, spectrographic observations indicated that tidal forces pull out streams of luminous gas which form whorls and bridges between the two stars.

If astronomers had to rely solely upon trigonometrical and spectroscopic parallaxes, the measurable stellar domain would be comparatively restricted. Fortunately there exist large numbers of variable stars known as CEPHEIDS whose light variations provide information about their distances. Many of them are at immense distances, even by astronomical standards, and they enable astronomers to extend their yardsticks to and indeed well beyond the distant stars of the Milky Way.

The cepheids are so-called after their prototype, δ Cephei, a star of approximately the third magnitude with a range of about 0·7 magnitude in a period of nearly $5\frac{1}{2}$ days. Their importance in distance determination arose when Miss Henrietta S. LEAVITT, of the Harvard College Observatory, discovered a remarkable relationship between their luminosity and length of period. Miss Leavitt found many of these stars in the Lesser MAGELLANIC

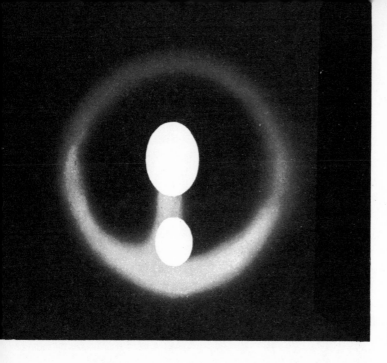

CLOUD, an object which to the unaided eye looks like a detached
fragment of the Milky Way and yet is actually an immense system of stars at present believed to be at a distance of some
230,000 light-years. The cepheids revealed themselves by their
light-curves – there was the small range in magnitude found in
δ Cephei and also the sharp rise to maximum brightness followed
by a slower decline to minimum brightness. The surprising thing
was that the period, with a range from one day to about 127 days,
could be correlated with apparent magnitude.

The relationship was so definite that when the periods were
plotted against the apparent magnitudes, the points defined a
smooth curve. The brightest stars had the longest periods and the
faintest stars had the shortest periods. Since the stars of the
Magellanic Cloud could be regarded as being all at the same great
distance, the bright stars of the cloud were really luminous and
the fainter stars were less luminous. Hence the curve became
known as the PERIOD-LUMINOSITY CURVE, for the relationship
could be regarded as one between period and luminosity.

Before the distances of cepheids in other parts of the sky could
be ascertained, it was necessary to assume that the period of any
cepheid accurately specified its luminosity. On this assumption

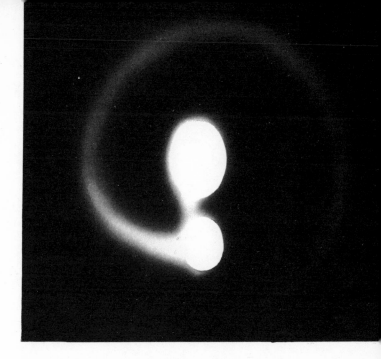

According to G. Kuiper
the star β Lyrae.

attempts were made to standardize the luminosity-period relationship, but uncertainties in the measurement of the distances of individual cepheids led to corresponding uncertainties regarding
the zero-point of the curve. Nevertheless, Harlow G. SHAPLEY
found that the relationship seemed to hold for all known cepheids,
and he accordingly used it to estimate the distances of the Lesser
and Greater Magellanic Clouds and many compact clusters of
stars known as GLOBULAR STAR CLUSTERS.

Shapley and his followers in this work were assisted by the fact
that, compared with the sun, the cepheids are all giant stars of
high luminosity. This meant that representatives several hundreds
of thousands of light-years away could be picked up and checked
for period of light variation. Unfortunately a duplicity is now
known to exist in the luminosity relationship: the single "curve"
can no longer be regarded as a line but rather as two curves. Some
cepheids (Type I) are about 1·5 magnitudes brighter than others
(Type II) of the same period, a difference which means that a
Type I cepheid is at about twice the distance of a Type II cepheid
of the same period and apparent brightness.

Cepheids, once thought to be eclipsing variables, are now
known to be pulsating stars. Their light variations are therefore

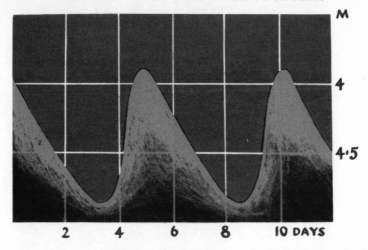

The light curve of δ Cephei. Its brightness decreases by about a magnitude and then rapidly increases again in a period of about 5 days 8 hours.

intrinsic properties of the stars themselves. A cepheid brightens as it expands and fades as it contracts, the maximum and minimum brightness occurring at the times of most rapid expansion and contraction respectively.

All the different kinds of stars so far mentioned have light variations which are regularly or irregularly periodic. There are, however, stars which undergo a spectacular rise in brightness and then slowly sink into almost complete obscurity. These are called NOVAE or temporary stars, but as the great majority of those so far recorded were originally faint stars, these names are misleading. In a few cases novae undergo semi-periodic outbursts every few decades. These are called RECURRENT NOVAE, and among them are the stars T Coronae Borealis, RS Ophiuchi and U Scorpii. Other novae can attain a brilliance so great that at maximum they are several hundred million times more luminous than the sun. These appear to undergo only one outburst and are called supernovae. The most famous are those of 1054, 1572 (Tycho's Nova) and 1604 (Kepler's Nova).

Although no two novae outbursts are alike, the majority have certain features in common. A fairly typical one occurred in June, 1918, when several observers discovered an apparently new star of

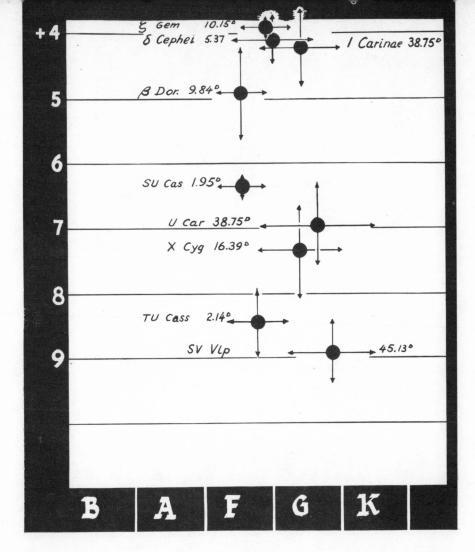

Above: Cepheid variables, showing variations in brightness (vertical range) and associated spectral changes (horizontal range). *Below:* Classical Cepheids are about 1½ magnitudes brighter than those of similar period belonging to Population II.

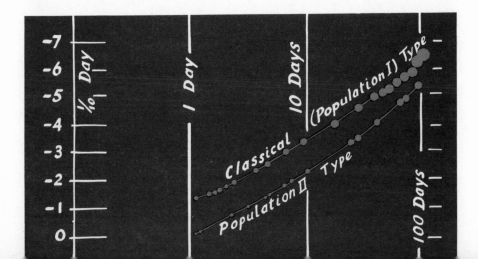

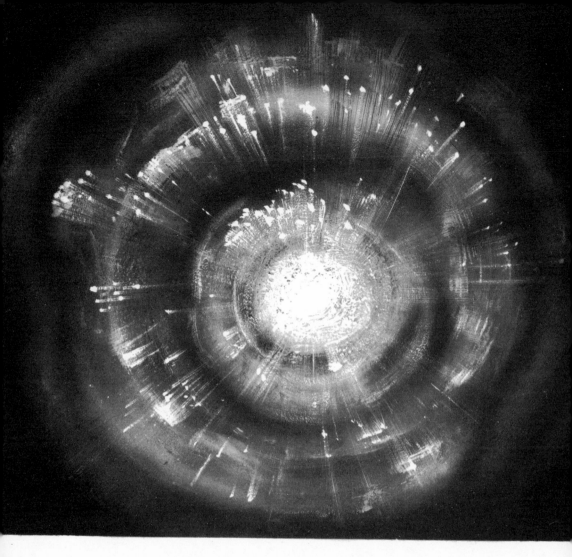

A nova or "new star" is really a star already in existence,
which explodes with tremendous violence.

about the first magnitude in the constellation of Aquila. A photograph of the region taken on June 5 showed the nova as a star of
magnitude 10·5, yet at maximum brilliance on June 9 the magnitude had changed to minus 1·2. In about 5 days the star therefore
underwent a 60,000-fold increase in brightness. This was followed
by a progressive decrease in brightness accompanied by semi-

periodic fluctuations, and by October, 1921, the star had reached the tenth magnitude. Nova Persei, 1901, had a similar rapid rise, and during its slow decline went through a series of light fluctuations which lasted for several months.

Associated with the dramatic rise in brightness of a typical nova is the drastic change in its spectrum. While brightening the star

The hot central star and expanding shell of gas of a nova. In the direction of the observer the radiation from the star undergoes selective absorption as it passes through the gas shell. The spectrum therefore contains absorption lines. The gas shell itself gives rise to emission lines. The lines are broadened owing to components of motion of the shell towards or away from the observer.

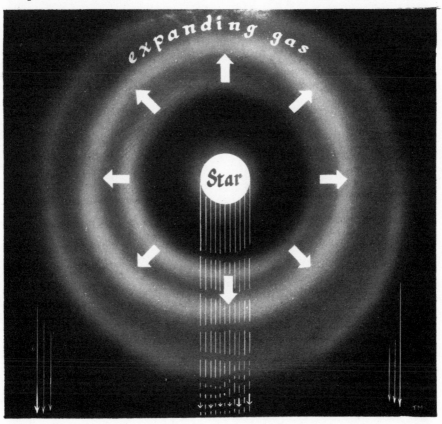

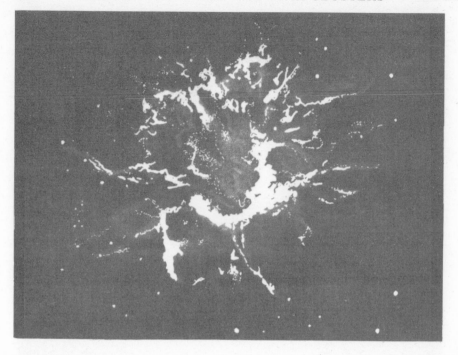

The Crab Nebula. Photographs in red light reveal a remarkable filamentary structure which gives the impression of violent activity.

appears of spectral class A (or B in the case of Nova Persei) with the lines all shifted towards the violet. This is clearly a Doppler-Fizeau effect, and it implies rapid motion towards the observer. The motion is best explained by supposing that the star is in rapid expansion, or better, that it has blown off its outer layers. With a supernova the explosion is even more violent, the star almost bursts and violently ejects all but the intensely hot central core.

After the main outburst the ejected material forms an expanding shell of gas. This is well shown in the case of the supernova observed by Chinese and Japanese astronomers from July 4, 1054 to April 17, 1056. It appeared in the constellation of Taurus, The Bull, and in a region in which the Crab Nebula now lies. There are good reasons for believing that the Crab Nebula, about 4000 light-years distant, is the remnant of the 1054 supernova. Spectrographic studies show that it is expanding at the fantastic rate of about 700 miles a second. The numerous tentacle-like filaments, well shown in red light, reach out into space for billions of miles and give an overall diameter estimated at six light-years. At the center are two small stars believed to be white dwarfs.

The Crab Nebula is a strong source of radio waves. It is also situated near the ecliptic, and in 1951 K. E. Machin and F. G. Smith suggested that the sun's annual close approach to it could be utilized for finding out more about the structure of the sun's outer atmosphere. The sun passes near the nebula every June, when the radio waves from the nebula have necessarily to travel through the outer corona. Recent observations of this so-called OCCULTATION

The Hyades (encircled by the dotted line) and Pleiades (upper right of the Hyades), two open star clusters in Taurus, The Bull.

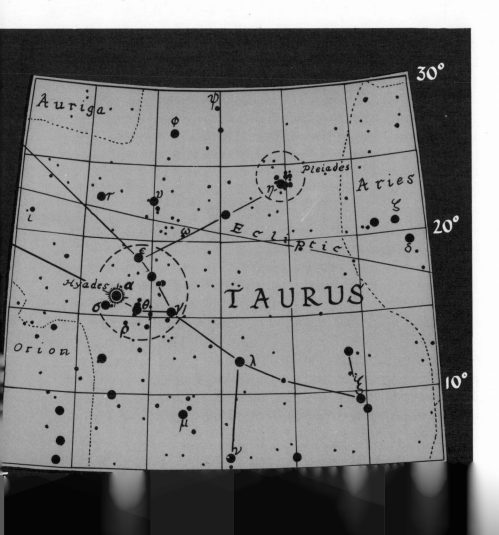

of a radio star by the sun show that the radio energy is both scattered and slightly refracted when it passes through the corona.

One of the most interesting discoveries of modern astronomy is the fact that stars do not have to appear close together to be physically associated. There are, for example, groups far larger than double and multiple systems whose components are scattered over immense volumes of space. These groups may consist of hundreds of stars and yet be so distant as to appear as misty patches to the unaided eye. Alternatively they can consist of a few dozen stars and form an array so open that it is difficult to imagine that the individuals are physically connected.

These star groups are called OPEN STAR CLUSTERS or GALAC-TIC CLUSTERS after the way they tend to occur in the region of the Milky Way. A well-known example is the Pleiades, a compact group of stars in the constellation of Taurus, The Bull. To the unaided eye the Pleiades appears as a little knot of six stars, but under favorable conditions a keen-sighted observer may discern 14 or even more stars. Binoculars greatly increase the number, and large telescopes show over two thousand stars.

For most Greek poets the Pleiades were seven stars which were changed into a flock of celestial doves to escape the amorous attentions of Orion, The Hunter. This is an appropriate comparison, for proper motion studies over many years have shown that the brighter stars of the group are all traveling in the same direction at a speed of about 25 miles a second. At this rate, and with their distances of approximately 450 light-years, the Pleiades would take about 33,000 years to move over an angular distance equal to the apparent diameter of the moon.

The English poet, Alfred Tennyson, described the Pleiades as "a swarm of fireflies tangled in a silver braid". The unaided eye sees the "fireflies" or highly luminous B-type stars. The other stars have a great range in size, luminosity and spectral type and get progressively redder with decreasing luminosity. The "silver braid", or veils of diffuse nebulosity in which the stars appear to be embedded, is best traced by the use of long-exposure photographs. This nebulosity was first detected visually in 1859 by Tempel, but he glimpsed only the faint glow near and around the star Merope. Modern photographs reveal that the entire cluster is involved in interstellar material which shines by reflecting and scattering the starlight. According to the results of radio observation at a wavelength of 21 centimeters, interaction between the cluster and the interstellar material gives rise to concentrations of neutral hydrogen.

The face of Taurus is formed by a conspicuous V-shaped array of stars known as the Hyades Cluster. This group appears to include the brilliant orange star Aldebaran, but this is not a member of the cluster and in fact is about half the distance away. The V-shaped array, moreover, is only the central part of a much larger cluster of stars which may comprise over 300 members.

Like the Pleiades, the Hyades cluster is a moving family of suns. Proper motion and radial velocity studies show that the members are all traveling with equal velocities in parallel paths inclined away from the sun. They therefore appear to have a convergent motion, first detected by Lewis Boss towards a point about 5° best of Betelgeuse.

The stars of the Big Dipper as they appear today.

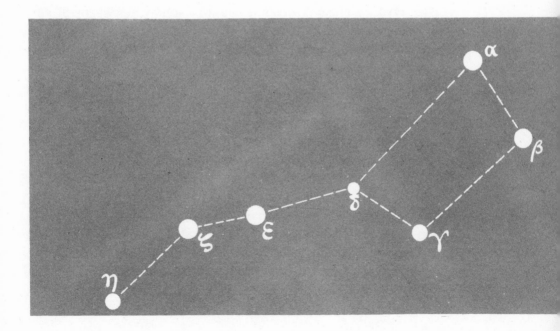

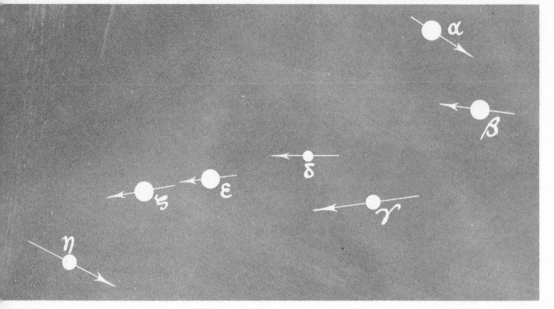

The directions of the proper motion of the stars of the Big Dipper.

The Hyades cluster forms a roughly spherical swarm of stars which is about 50 light-years across and is centered some 120 light-years from the sun. In this giant system the brightest stars are giants of Class K – stars, that is, which are cooler and less luminous than the brightest stars in the Pleiades. The great majority are main-sequence stars and a few are red giants, but none are luminous enough to produce reflection nebulosity should insterstellar material be present.

When an open cluster is very near, its members can be found in widely separated parts of the sky. This is the case with the Ursa Major Cluster, so-called because five of the seven stars of The Big Dipper lie near its center. Proper motion studies show that the seven stars, with the exception of the first star in the bowl and the last star in the handle, are all traveling in the same direction at the same speed. This means that these seven are leaving The Big Dipper configuration, but so slowly that the change will not become perceptible to the unaided eye until many centuries have passed.

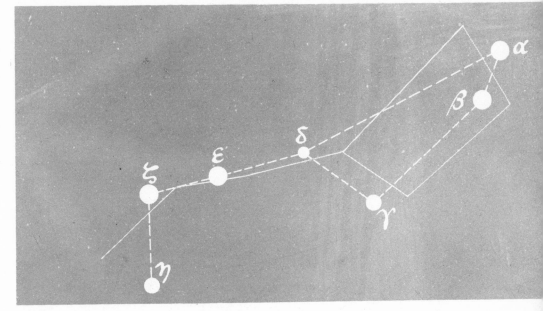

The change in appearance of the Big Dipper in the next 100,000 years, with its stars superimposed on the corresponding pattern formed by the same stars today.

Strange to say, Sirius and other stars in different parts of the sky are members of the cluster, which according to W. M. SMART, contains at least 42 members.

Unlike the Pleiades and Hyades, the great majority of star clusters cannot be resolved into stars by the unaided eye and therefore appear as faint, misty patches in the sky. They were first catalogued by the French astronomer Charles MESSIER, whose main interest was the discovery of comets. While searching for comets Messier came across many nebulous objects which were not comets at all but permanent features of the starry background. To avoid mistaking them for comets he drew up a list of 103 objects which included several open star clusters and many nebulous patches which could not be resolved into stars by his small telescope. Some of these "nébuleuses sans étoiles" are now known to be compact swarms of stars called globular star clusters. In these the stars number many thousands and form a tightly-knit and almost spherical ball. They are brightest at the center, where

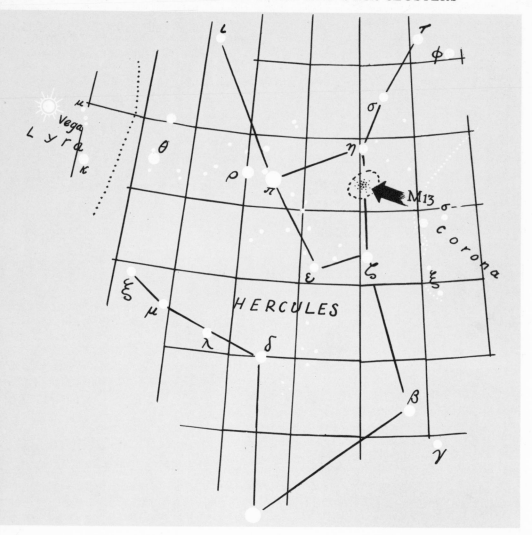

The great northern globular cluster M13 in Hercules can readily be located and detected with a field glass or binoculars.

the immense number of stars gives the impression, at least on photographs, of a solid starry mass.

The finest globular cluster in northern skies is Messier 13, or the thirteenth object in Messier's list. This lies in a comparatively barren region of the sky in the constellation of Hercules. To the naked eye it is just visible on the clearest nights as a faint, hazy

A globular star cluster.

star. "This is but a little patch" wrote Halley in 1716, "but it shows itself to the naked eye when the sky is serene and the moon absent". Through a small telescope it could easily be mistaken for a distant comet. Sir William Herschel, who observed it through his large reflecting telescopes, estimated that 14,000 stars were "cribb'd, cabined and confined" in Halley's "little patch".

Modern telescopes reveal that Messier 13 contains at least 50,000 stars and probably ten times this number. So great is its distance that its light takes some 31,000 years to reach us. It is therefore far beyond the bright stars in the constellation of Hercules, and in comparison the Pleiades and Hyades star clusters are quite near objects. In size it is about 160 light-years across, so while the center appears to be a tight stellar ball, the stars in even the most crowded parts are separated from each other by many millions of miles. Looking at photographs of this and other globular clusters we have constantly to remind ourselves that each of

The night sky from within a globular cluster looking towards the Galaxy would reveal thousands of dazzlingly brilliant stars belonging to the cluster superimposed on it.

the larger star images represents a giant reddish star far larger and as much as a thousandfold brighter than our own sun.

If one of the stars well inside the cluster is accompanied by a planet or even a family of planets, the sky as seen from such a planet would be splendid indeed. Not only would the stars change perceptibly in position and brightness within a human lifetime, but many would shine so brilliantly that collectively they would turn night almost into day.

Although Messier 13 is a magnificent object of its type, it is rivalled in size and brightness by a globular cluster in the southern hemisphere, about 22,000 light-years distant and known as ω Centauri. This was discovered in 1677 by Halley who was then at St Helena engaged in observing the stars of southern skies. To the naked eye it looks like a misty star, but on photographs its full extent can be traced over an area of the sky equal to that of the disk of the full moon. Here again the total number of stars in the cluster probably runs into millions. Another fine naked-eye globular cluster in the southern hemisphere is 47 Toucani, located near the Lesser Magellanic Cloud.

A valuable characteristic of many globular star clusters lies in the fact that they contain a number of long-period or "classical" cepheids as well as short-period variable stars. By assuming that the "classical" cepheids in the cluster were identical with local cepheids, Shapley was able to estimate the distances of many globular clusters. He could then determine the absolute magnitudes of the short-period variables which at the time were called CLUSTER-TYPE VARIABLES and were believed to be restricted to globular clusters. They are now found in all parts of the sky and are called RR Lyrae stars after the seventh magnitude star RR Lyrae, their brightest member.

RR Lyrae stars have an average period of about 12 hours and the general pattern of their light changes is not unlike that of the long-period cepheids. They are now known to form a distinct class or group of stars whose importance in distance-determina-

A field of globular star clusters. 31 globular clusters (about one-third of the total number visible in the entire sky) are found in this particular part of the sky.

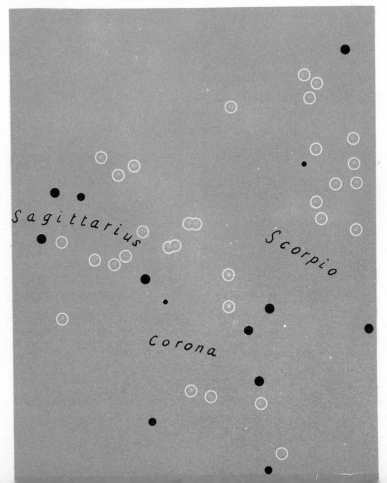

tion lies not in their cepheid characteristics but in the fact that they are all of about the same luminosity and have an absolute magnitude of o·o. Once an RR Lyrae star has been detected (by virtue of its short and very regular period), measurement of its apparent brightness leads directly to an estimation of its distance.

The distance of globular clusters can also be estimated by taking advantage of the brightest stars in them. These are typical red giants whose absolute visual magnitude is presumably about −2, or the same as that for similar stars elsewhere. A further check is provided by assuming that all globular star clusters are equal in size. If a cluster has an angular diameter one-half that of another, it is most likely to be at about twice the distance.

Altogether about 100 globular clusters have been discovered. They appear in all parts of the sky with the exception of the band of the Milky Way. However, they are most common in southern skies and appear to form a spherical group of immense extent with its center in the direction of the rich star-fields of the constellation of Sagittarius, The Archer. The significance of this distribution will be made clear in the following chapters.

An artist's impression of the Milky Way System from the outside, showing Population I, Population II and globular star clusters.

9. Our galaxy, the Milky Way

Among the various nebulous objects listed by Messier was one in the constellation of Andromeda which had a wholly misty appearance even when examined through a telescope. Simon MARIUS in 1612 had compared its appearance to that of a candle flame seen through translucent horn. A similar object, called The Great Nebula in Orion, was discovered by Huygens in 1656. He came across it while examining θ Orionis or Theta Orionis, the middle star of the sword of Orion. The star appeared multiple and with others seemed to shine through a nebulosity which Huygens likened to "an opening in the sky through which a brighter region was visible". Thereafter both objects were carefully observed, but every increase in telescope aperture and magnification failed to resolve them into stars.

During his great reviews or surveys of the stars, Sir William Herschel found that this apparently non-stellar nature was shared by many hundreds of other objects which, he thought, were either large tracts of shining fluid or star clusters so remote as completely to escape resolution. By 1802 Herschel had drawn up catalogues of 2500 nebulae and clusters – the term nebulae was given to all those objects which could not be resolved into stars. His son Sir John HERSCHEL continued this work by surveying southern skies with a reflecting telescope of 18 inches aperture. In 1864 the *General Catalogue of Nebulae* was published; this listed 5079

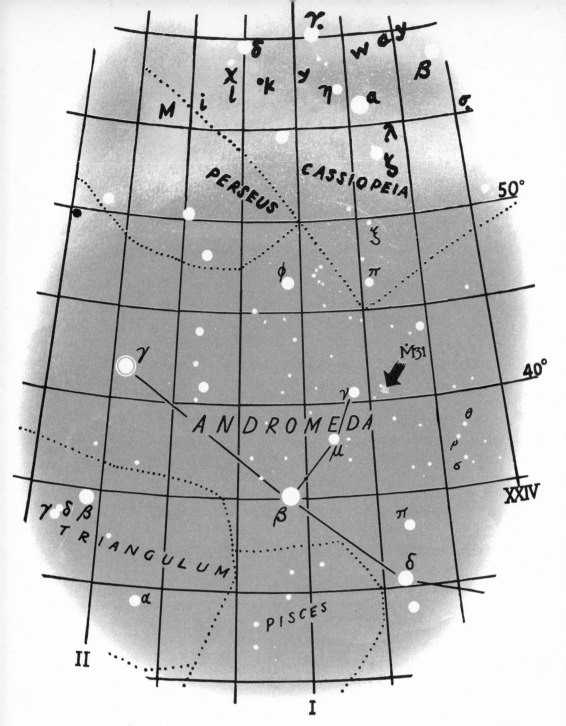

The location of M31, a great galaxy in Andromeda, which to the unaided eye appears as a faint misty patch of light.

objects of which only 450 had been discovered by observers other than the Herschels. This list formed the basis of John Dreyer's *New General Catalogue* (abbreviated *N.G.C.*) issued by the Royal Astronomical Society of London in 1888, which contained, along with additional *Index Catalogues*, well over 10,000 objects.

Meanwhile a completely new line of attack was devised by Sir William Huggins. In 1864 he turned his 8-inch refractor equipped with a spectroscope to N.G.C. 6543, a small bright elliptical nebula in the constellation of Draco, The Dragon. Imagine Huggins' surprise when, on looking into the eyepiece of the spectroscope, the light of the nebula, instead of being spread out in a band as in the stars, was concentrated in a line in the green and in two fainter lines in the blue-green. "The riddle of the nebulae was solved", he wrote. "The answer, which had come to us in the light itself, read: Not an aggregation of stars, but a luminous gas." Diffuse or IRREGULAR NEBULAE like the Great Nebula in Orion

The Great Nebula in Orion lies near the star θ Orionis.

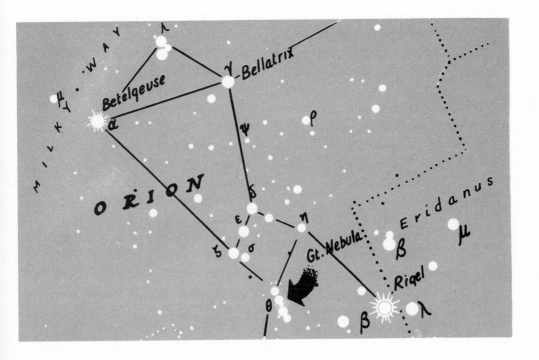

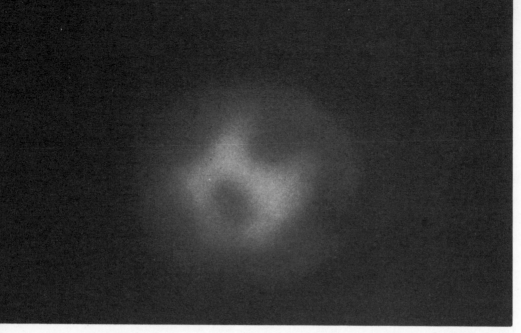

Planetary nebulae are so called because they have a disk-shaped appearance.

also gave emission spectra, but the one in Andromeda (Messier 31 or M31) presented a continuous stellar-type spectrum. Subsequent studies, aided by direct photography and spectrography, fully confirmed Huggins' conclusion that there are two main types of nebulae, one gaseous, the other a complex of stars.

Our concern in this chapter is with interstellar material and therefore with gaseous nebulae. Their most spectacular representative is The Great Nebula in Orion (M42 and M43). This derives its light from the stars embedded in it, and in particular from the four stars which form a compact group known as the "Trapezium". These intensely hot O- and B-type stars are particularly rich in radiation of the short violet and ultra-violet wavelengths. This radiation is absorbed by the surrounding gases and selectively emitted at longer wavelengths, a process known as fluorescence and one already mentioned in connection with comets' tails (see page 149).

A similar process is also in operation in PLANETARY NEBULAE. These are so-called because visually they have a pale uniform aspect not unlike the telescopic image of Uranus. Their roundish shapes arise from the fact that they are vast spheres or rings of gas, excited into fluorescence by an extremely hot central star. They appear small because of their immense distances: a typical planetary nebula may have a diameter of a million million miles, but at distances of 3000 to 30,000 light-years it appears as only a small disk even on large-scale photographs. In some planetary nebulae the gaseous envelope takes the form of a hollow shell, which on account of perspective appears as a luminous annulus or ring. The most prominent of these annular types is M57 in the constellation of Lyra, The Lyre, and its ring form can be readily detected in telescopes of modest aperture.

Spectroscopic observations show that the shells or envelopes of many of the 150 known planetary nebulae are expanding. The rate of expansion is extremely slow compared with those found for several old novae, but the fact that expansion is taking place adds weight to the hypothesis that a planetary nebula, with its hot, central star, may well be a former nova or supernova.

Unable to identify the bright green line in the spectrum of the planetary nebula in Draco, Huggins postulated a mysterious "NEBULIUM", unknown on earth. Since his time a great deal of work has been done towards identifying this and other lines in the spectra of nebulae. There is now no need to invoke "nebulium", for all the lines can be accounted for in terms of neutral hydrogen, neutral and ionized helium, and unusual or "forbidden" transitions in atoms of oxygen, nitrogen, neon and sulphur.

For any one given telescope and speed of photographic plate, the photographic appearance of a nebula depends mainly on time of exposure. The brighter central regions of, say, the Orion Nebula, are best shown when exposure times are comparatively short, but the object then appears relatively small. Its fainter and more extended parts appear when exposure times are increased, but at the expense of losing by over-exposure the details in the central portion and the stars of the Trapezium. Long exposures, however, reveal that this chaotic mass of fluorescent gas covers an immense region. They also suggest that the gas in the central parts is quite dense, whereas in actuality the whole structure must be extremely tenuous. Indeed, if the earth could suddenly be immersed in it, we should hardly be aware of the fact. The nebula appears bright more because of its vast extent than because of its proximity, for, according to recent estimates, its distance is over 900 light-years.

The regions surrounding the Orion Nebula contain great clouds of non-luminous interstellar material, believed to consist of both gas and dust. This is apparent in the region of θ Orionis, where a dark wedge, often referred to as the "Fish-mouth", is apparently driven into the Orion Nebula. This effect is brought about by the absorption of light – the interstellar material between us and the bright nebula acts as a highly effective obscuring screen. Similar effects are also well shown around and just south of ʒ Orionis, one of the three stars in Orion's belt. Photographs show a vast complex of bright and dark nebulae whose filaments and whorls are inextricably interwoven. Also conspicuous in this area is the "Horsehead Nebula" formed by a great obscuring mass seen by projection against the luminous background.

As E. E. Barnard first showed, a surprising number of extended obscuring clouds appear on photographs of the Milky Way. Some make conspicuous black projections on bright areas of nebulosity,

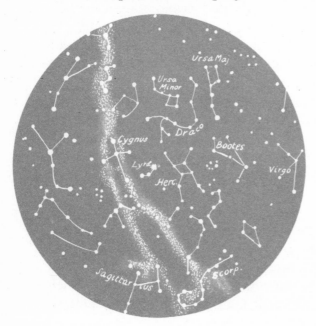

On September evenings the Milky Way arches high across the northern hemisphere of the sky. On a clear night the great rifts shown in the drawing can be clearly seen. These are the greatest of the dark nebulae.

Circular patches of dark nebulosity obscuring the stars beyond them appear like "holes in the sky". The drawing shows a typical "coal sack".

others blot out almost completely the light of the more distant stars and look like great blots of ink on the starry background. Many appear to be sprinkled with stars, but this is generally a line-of-sight effect because these stars are between us and the dark nebulae. But all provide striking confirmation of the interdependence of stars and bright nebulae. If no high-temperature stars existed in or near the great clouds of interstellar gas and cosmic dust, all nebulae would be dark nebulae.

In the northern hemisphere the richest region for gaseous clouds lies in Cygnus and the surrounding constellations. Here are found the "North America" and "Pelican" Nebulae, separated from each other by a dark lane of interstellar absorption located near the star Deneb, or α Cygni. Details of this vast complex are strikingly shown on red-sensitive plates exposed behind red filters in the 48-inch Palomar Schmidt telescope, for these record the Hα radiation or hydrogen emission of the gas clouds. This selective photography gives most effective impressions of the famous Veil Nebula or Loop Nebula in Cygnus, whose intricate filamentary wreaths and streamers of luminous hydrogen form a broken and expanding annulus. According to some astronomers the Loop Nebula is the perspective effect of a hollow gas shell about 50 light-years across, the remains perhaps of an ancient supernova explosion. Attempts to find the hot central star, however, have so far met with no success, and the wisps of nebulosity may well derive their light from the collision of the expanding shell with interstellar clouds.

In the southern hemisphere one of the most spectacular bright nebulae is in the Milky Way region, near the variable star η Carinae. As portrayed on photographs taken in red light, this object is diversified by obscuring rifts and lanes, the main "islands" being intricately interwoven with both bright and dark nebulosities. Further along the Milky Way are the stars of the Southern Cross, and beside them, the Coalsack, one of most striking dark nebulae. This occurs in a region devoid of bright nebulosity, and in contrast with the brilliant reaches of the Milky Way all around, looks like an intensely black cloud and even like a hole in the heavens. At a distance of about 400 light-years, the Coalsack is one of the nearer nebulae, consequently few foreground stars are projected on its surface. Its inky darkness is also broken by small patches of bright nebulosity which lie in the regions beyond and whose light is finding gaps in the otherwise almost completely obscuring barrier.

Since reflection nebulosity (as in the Pleiades) and emission nebulosity (as in the Orion Nebula) arise from the presence of immense volumes of interstellar material, it is natural to enquire whether this material in extremely rare form extends throughout space. The first pointer that this is in fact the case came in 1904, when G. Hartmann found that the sharp K line of ionized calcium in the spectrum of the spectroscopic binary δ Orionis did not vary at all during the periodic change in the star's radial velo-

The Crab Nebula. Photographs in red light reveal a remarkable filamentary

city. Similar stationary H and K calcium lines were later found in
the spectra of other stars. This encouraged the view that these
stars are surrounded by stationary clouds of calcium. In 1926,
however, A. S. Eddington, introducing the idea of the cosmic
cloud, suggested that it was universal, filling the whole of interstellar space. On this basis the absorption appeared only with
certain types of stars because only those types were sufficiently
luminous to give observable spectra at distances allowing
observable absorption.

Observational evidence that calcium gas is not restricted to the locality of certain stars but is spread throughout the intervening space came in 1928, when O. STRUVE found that the apparent intensity of the H and K lines of ionized calcium increases with the distance of the star. In addition, stationary lines, now called INTERSTELLAR LINES, were found for neutral sodium, neutral potassium, neutral iron and ionized titanium, and also for molecules of the hydrocarbon and cyanogen radicals. More abundant than any of these, however, is hydrogen, observable directly through its red Hα emission and also by radio observations at 21 centimeters wavelength. Both techniques show that the hydrogen gas is not spread uniformly throughout space but forms separate interstellar clouds in a rarer substratum, an arrangement which the other gases appear also to share.

Mixed with the gas clouds are vast quantities of cosmic dust which have both a scattering and an absorbing effect on starlight. Unless allowed for, this effect could seriously upset the estimated distances of all but the sun's neighbors. If the scattering was great, distant stars would appear dimmed and reddened due to distance alone, while extremely distant objects might not be seen at all. As Shapley once pointed out, if the light loss due to absorption and scattering in space should be as much as one-millionth of one per cent in every 100 million miles, stars 3500 light-years away would appear about two magnitudes too faint.

The ring nebula in Lyra.

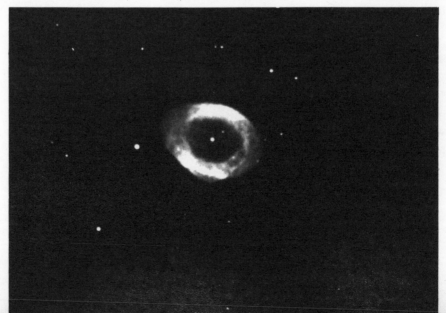

The "Horsehead" Nebula in Orion south of the star ζ Orionis. Photographed in red light with the 200-inch Hale telescope.

The reddening effect of INTERSTELLAR DUST is well brought out by photographing some regions of the sky in blue light and then in more penetrating infra-red radiation. On infra-red plates appear stars, globular clusters and distant nebulae which are only faintly shown or even entirely absent on ordinary blue plates. The dust also gives a reddish hue to certain otherwise bluish-white B-type stars which lie in the direction of the Milky Way. Astronomers allow for this when assigning distances to these stars and describe it in terms of a difference called COLOR EXCESS. It is certain that the dust is strongly condensed towards the plane of the Milky Way, but the condensation is far from uniform and the dust, like the gas, forms isolated clouds of immense extent.

Seen through clear dark skies in both hemispheres, the Milky Way appears among the stars as a continuous path of pearly

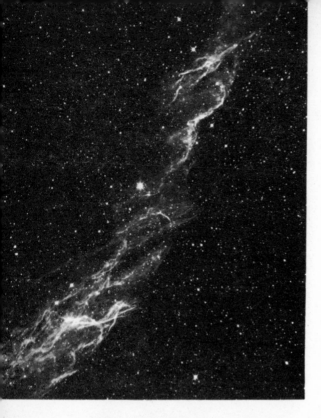

Central part of an extensive fila-
mentous nebula in Cygnus. Photographed with the 60-inch telescope
of the Mount Wilson and Palomar
Observatories.

light. It was first traced and described in scientific terms by
Ptolemy, who saw that, far from being uniform in width and
brightness, it had a patchy appearance. In the constellations of
Auriga and Taurus it narrowed down almost to nothing, and was
divided into two parts by a dark rift between Cygnus and Sagittarius. Any idea of its starry nature, however, could not be checked
by naked-eye observations alone.

As soon as Galileo looked at the Milky Way through his small
telescope he saw that it is composed of innumerable faint stars.
Today, and with the aid of giant photographic telescopes, the Milky
Way lies revealed in all its incomparable splendour. The exposed
plates reveal myriads of stars which in some regions are so
numerous and apparently so close together that their images merge
into one another to form great diffuse star clouds. In other parts
the stars are set in heavy folds and wreaths of bright nebulosity.
In others they are hidden by patches, streaks and rifts of obscuring interstellar clouds. From the photographic evidence alone it is
therefore clear that the Milky Way does not consist of stars alone,
but of stars, interstellar gas and cosmic dust.

So much, then, for the general appearance of the Milky Way, but what of its form and nature? Does it actually consist, as Galileo once wrote, of "nothing else but a mass of innumerable stars planted together in clusters"? The first to put this idea to the test of observation was Sir William Herschel, whose greatest enterprise was "to obtain a knowledge of the structure of the heavens". With his reflector of $18\frac{1}{2}$ inches aperture he instituted "star gauges" or systematic counts of the number of stars in different parts of the sky. As a result he concluded in 1785 that the Milky Way is an effect of perspective brought about by the sun's position in "a very extensive, branching, compound congeries of many millions of stars". He sketched the system as a thin disk of irregular outline and with a deep cleft to account for the two branches of the Milky Way between Cygnus and Scorpio. The sun, he thought, was near the center. Hence when we look outwards towards the periphery of the disk we look through a great

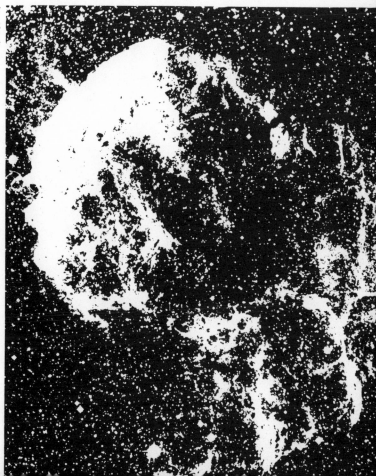

Study of the detail in many of the nebulae suggests great violence of movement.

extent or depth of stars. In this direction stars appear to be banked on stars until their number at first glance appear to be limitless, but in directions at right angles they thin out rapidly and we soon reach the limits of the system.

The disk theory, incidentally, did not originate with Herschel, for it had been advocated by Thomas WRIGHT of Durham in 1750 and also by Immanuel KANT and Johann H. LAMBERT, but as a mere guess. Herschel, on the other hand, supported the idea with solid observational evidence. Yet after further investigations he modified his earlier views and suggested that the system was far more extended towards the periphery than he had originally supposed. "The utmost stretch of the space-penetrating power of the twenty-foot telescope" he wrote in 1818, "could not fathom the profundity of the Milky Way".

The disk-like system of stars, called by Herschel "our nebula", is now known as the Milky Way System, or more briefly, as the

The absorption of starlight by interstellar dust causes some stars to appear fainter than they would otherwise be if space was transparent.

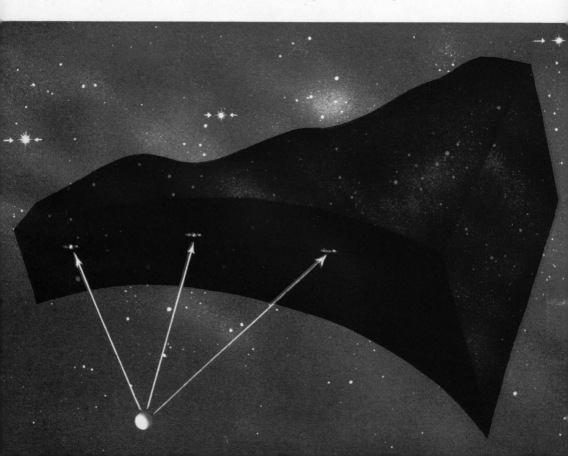

Galaxy. The plane of the disk is the GALACTIC PLANE, and the directions at right angles to this are those of the GALACTIC POLES. The central line of the Milky Way does not, however, coincide with the galactic plane but is slightly shifted towards the south galactic pole: this indicates that the sun lies a little to the north of the galactic plane.

During the present century a variety of methods has been used to estimate the dimensions of the Galaxy. In 1900 only about 60 stellar parallaxes were known by the trigonometrical method, but after 1901, and as the result of a suggestion made by the Dutch astronomer Jacobus KAPTEYN, a new method of distance determination was pressed into service. This took advantage of the sun's motion in space, which causes stars at a given distance and direction all to have a common PARALLACTIC MOTION, or component of their observed proper motion. By averaging the motions of stars of similar brightness and spectral type their mean parallaxes can be estimated. Then came the method of spectroscopic parallaxes (page 173) – a method which enabled Adams and others to push the distance scale outwards to several thousands of light-years. Also important in this connection were studies of eclipsing binaries, cepheids, and highly luminous B-type stars of known absolute magnitude. There followed Shapley's pioneer work in fixing the positions in space of most of the known globular clusters, showing thereby something of the immense extent of this particular sub-system.

Out of these and other investigations has emerged a picture of the Galaxy which in size, complexity and overall grandeur surpasses the most ambitious of earlier models. In general form the galactic system is believed to be a flattened disk-shaped complex of stars, gas and dust so stupendous in size that light would take over 100,000 years to traverse its longer diameter and about one-tenth of that time to traverse its thickness. The stars are by no means uniformly distributed within this space but at any given distance from the center tend to cluster in and around the galactic plane. In number they thin out with increasing distance from the center. At the center, in the direction of Sagittarius, where the star density is greatest, lies the great bulge of the core or nucleus,

A schematic cross-section of the Galaxy with the sun embedded in the outer spiral portion and the whole surrounded by the system of globular clusters.

believed to consist almost wholly of stars. Here the star fields are brightest of all and the structure of stars and dust clouds is most complex. The sun, a fairly average, faint, and inconspicuous star among tens of billions of other stars, lies near the galactic plane but about 27,000 light-years from the center. From our position near the sun we therefore see but a small part of the Galaxy – the greater part is hidden by immense clouds of obscuring material which, like the stars, congregate in and near the galactic plane.

The system has no well-defined boundary, for the star density continues to decrease beyond its main confines to form a faint haze of stars. Also beyond the main system are the globular clusters, distributed fairly uniformly in a roughly spherical volume of diameter about 150,000 light-years and found by Shapley to be centered on the great star clouds in Sagittarius.

The flattened form of the Galaxy implies that it is rotating around the central nucleus. This must act as the mass center and, if the stars did not revolve around it, they would be drawn towards it – the system would collapse inwards upon itself. Conclusive demonstration that rotation is taking place was first given in 1927 by the Dutch astronomer, J. Oort. As a result of a statistical analysis of the radial velocities and proper motions of a large number of highly luminous stars, Oort obtained evidence of the differential effect produced by the rotation. Stars further out from the galactic center than the sun appear to lag behind, stars nearer the center appear to forge ahead of the sun. The effect clearly arises from the general characteristic that the greater the distance of a star from the center, the less is its orbital velocity. In this respect the stars in the Galaxy are like the planets in the solar system – those nearest to the mass center move faster than those further away. The sun and the stars in its vicinity have orbital speeds of about 140 miles a second and, at a distance of approximately 27,000 light-years from the center, take something like 200 million years to complete one revolution.

Is the Galaxy the one and only system of its kind, or is it just one of many similar systems? Sir William Herschel in 1785 expressed the view that the nebulae which his telescopes failed to resolve were all vast aggregations of stars far beyond the bound-

Changes in the relative positions of stars (A and B) near the sun owing to differential velocities or rotation within the Galaxy.

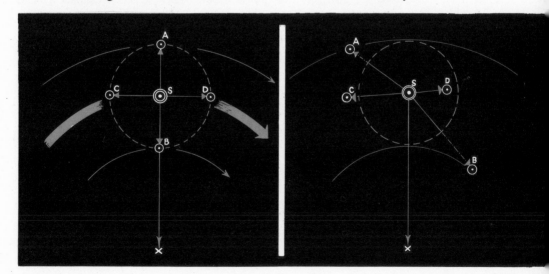

ary of the Galaxy as determined by his star gauges. This view he modified in later years, for although he had no means of deriving the distances of nebulae he felt certain that some of them consisted not of stars but of some fairly uniform shining fluid. That this later view was largely correct was indicated by Sir William Huggins' discovery that the Orion Nebula and several others show the bright-line spectrum of a glowing gas. These objects were accordingly brought back into the Galaxy, but doubts still remained about the nature and status of nebulae which, like M31 in Andromeda, lie well outside the belt of the Milky Way and give absorption- or solar-type spectra.

The need to resolve these doubts loomed into increasing prominence with the rapid development of astronomical photography. In the mid-nineteenth century, visual observations made with Lord Rosse's great 6-foot reflecting telescope had revealed curved filaments of nebulosity in the nebula M51 in Canes Venatici. These filaments gave it a spiral form, an appearance strikingly shown on early celestial photographs and in particular on those secured by George Willis RITCHEY in the late 1890s with a 24-inch reflector at the Yerkes Observatory. A spiral form was also indicated in photographs of M31 in Andromeda and M33 in Triangulum, two objects which came to be regarded as the largest of the spiral nebulae. A further significant step arose from photographs obtained by James Keeler with the 36-inch Crossley reflector at the Lick Observatory. These revealed, for the first time and in all parts of the sky except in the Milky Way, the existence of an immense number of either very small or very distant symmetrical nebulae. Large objects like Messier 31 and Messier 33 were either rare, or if small image size was interpreted as large distance, the observable domain was much larger than hitherto realized.

After the completion of the 60-inch reflector at the Mount Wilson Observatory in 1908, Ritchey obtained with it splendid photographs of M31. These showed more clearly than ever before the spiral structure and granulations in the spiral arms which he described as "great numbers of soft, star-like condensations". On photographs taken with the 100-inch Hooker reflector at Mount

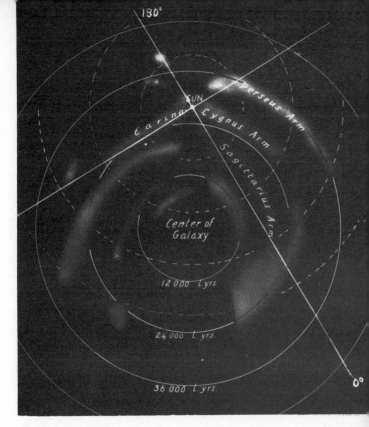

Local part of the Galaxy determined by radio-astronomical observations.

Wilson these granulations appeared as star images and clusters of star images – the spiral arms were composed of swarms of stars.

In 1925, and after a careful study of plates taken with the 100-inch reflector, Edwin P. HUBBLE discovered that a number of the stars in the outer parts of Messier 31 and Messier 33 showed typical cepheid variation. From a study of their periods and brightnesses, and as Shapley had done previously for the globular clusters, he deduced their actual luminosities and distances. Both Messier 31 and Messier 33 turned out to be at about the same distance, estimated by Hubble to be about 800,000 light-years. Both objects are therefore independent stellar systems far beyond the Galaxy and its system of globular clusters. Hubble then proceeded to show that Messier 31 and Messier 33 are comparatively near objects as galaxies go and that each of the innumerable faint nebulae first recorded by Keeler was in fact an incredibly remote galaxy. Not only is the sun an insignificant unit in the Galaxy, but the Galaxy is but one unit of the stupendous system of EXTRA-GALACTIC NEBULAE or galaxies which constitutes the whole observable domain.

Since Messier 31 and many other galaxies have a well-defined spiral structure it is natural to inquire whether evidence could be found for a similar structure in the Galaxy. At first sight it would appear that the sun is most unfavourably placed for studies of this kind. The great dust clouds prevent our seeing very far along the main plane and almost completely hide the nucleus from view. In 1951, however, W. W. Morgan investigated the distribution in distance of highly luminous O- and B-type stars along the northern Milky Way, and the first vestiges of three spiral arms became discernible. This information has since been greatly supplemented by the results of radio observations conducted at the 21-centimeter wavelength (or 1420 MEGACYCLES per second frequency) of neutral hydrogen. These waves pass without hindrance through interstellar dust, and like those in the optical range, can carry the tell-tale signs of the Doppler-Fizeau effect: they change in frequency (and hence in wavelength) according to the relative speed of approach or recession of the source. It is therefore possible to determine from signal intensities at wavelengths at or near 21 centimeters the concentration and radial velocities of neutral hydrogen clouds in different parts of the Milky Way. This information can then be built into a model which takes into account the sun's position and also the most likely way in which the velocity of galactic rotation varies with distance from the center. According to the results so far obtained by the joint labors of astronomers in the Netherlands and in Sydney, Australia, the sun is situated near the inner edge of a spiral arm many thousands of light-years long. This arm stretches away from the sun towards the stars of Cygnus and contains the Orion Nebula and the blue giant stars of Orion. The arm appears to be most distant from the galactic nucleus in the direction of the sun: elsewhere it curves inwards in the direction of galactic rotation to reach finally a distance of about 21,000 light-years from the center.

Above: the Great Spiral Galaxy in Andromeda (Messier 31) as seen through the 48-inch Schmidt telescope. *Left:* photograph in yellow light of one of the elliptical satellite galaxies, taken with the 200-inch Hale telescope. *Right:* the southern region of Messier 31 showing the high-luminosity stars in the spiral arm. (200-inch Hale telescope photograph.)

10. Beyond the Milky Way

The great Andromeda spiral M31 has probably been studied more than any other spiral, with the exception, of course, of our own Galaxy. It is certainly the most impressive object in the heavens, both in regard to its overall aspect and in the variety and complexity of its details. Visually, however, it is disappointing, even when examined with very large telescopes: the spiral arms cannot then be seen and the whole object looks like a misty patch whose longest extent is only about 2°. Yet by using a delicate photo-electric method, Stebbins and Whitford have been able to trace its apparent diameter over some 7·5°, thereby making its actual diameter about one-eighth of its distance. But apart from this M31 is essentially an object for photographic study, and nearly all of our knowledge about it has been obtained from the careful scrutiny of photographic plates.

The system has an elliptical outline, but this arises from the fact that its circular form is seen in perspective with its plane inclined at about 15° to the line of sight. This adds to the difficulty of resolving the individual parts, but even so a surprising variety of objects has been discovered and studied. Many more cepheids have been found since Hubble first used them for distance-estimation purposes. Their periods range between 10 and 50 days and their magnitudes from 19·3 to 18·3. Like galactic cepheids they are stars of high luminosity and fit the Type I period-luminosity curve. Furthermore, over 100 novae have appeared in Messier 31 in the past 40 years, plus one supernova which was discovered by Gully in 1885 and rose at maximum to the seventh magnitude. In addition, photographs of the spiral arms reveal star clusters, bright supergiant stars and emission nebulae – objects, that is, which are similar to their counterparts in and near the plane of our own Galaxy and which are likewise involved in interstellar haze and dust. Messier 31 is also accompanied by globular clusters which form a system comparable in size to that associated with the Galaxy. These were studied by Hubble in 1931 and were found to have their upper limit of luminosity about 1·5 magnitudes fainter than the upper limit of the globular clusters in the Galaxy, a discrepancy which was destined to have far-reaching consequences.

For some curious reason, and despite increases in plate sensitivity and telescope power, the nucleus of Messier 31 defied resolution into individual stars. The limit of the 100-inch with blue-sensitive plates had already been pushed to the extreme when Baade decided to see whether red-sensitive plates would be more effective. In the fall of 1943, with Andromeda in the zenith, and using red-sensitive plates, Baade gave exposures of about four hours each on the nucleus of Messier 31. His skill and patience were most amply rewarded. Not only was the central region resolved into myriads of stars, but also the two satellite elliptical galaxies Messier 32 and NGC 205, thereby indicating that the stars in them are not blue stars at all but highly-luminous red stars.

These stars were found to be about equal in luminosity to the red giants in globular clusters and yet distinctly more luminous than the red giants in the sun's vicinity. From this and other considerations Baade concluded that there are two distinct populations of stars. Representatives of the first system, called POPULATION I form the arms of spiral galaxies and the Magellanic Clouds. This system therefore contains not only the highly luminous O- and B-type supergiant stars of galactic clusters and the arms of spiral galaxies, but also interstellar dust and emission nebulae. The sun, located in a spiral arm, is therefore a member of Population I. In the second system, POPULATION II, are the red supergiants of globular clusters and the central regions of spiral galaxies – regions, that is, which are in themselves free from the obscuring effects of interstellar dust.

The two populations are well shown in photographs of Messier 31 taken first on blue-sensitive plates and then on infra-red sensitive plates. In the first the spiral form is clearly shown, being picked out in the main by the hot blue stars, but the central regions remain comparatively featureless. In the second the spiral arms vanish completely, and the galaxy appears as a haze of individual stars heavily concentrated in the center and thinning rapidly away from the nucleus. So great is the number of these Population II stars that over four-fifths of the total light emitted by the galaxy comes from them, which is a surprising result when we consider the prominence of the bright blue stars in ordinary photographs.

One group of stars in Messier 31 consistently eluded discovery. These were the RR Lyrae stars, which because of their absolute magnitude, 0·0, should have just appeared at the photographic limit of the 200-inch telescope. Since they could not be detected, it was apparent that the spiral was much further away than the estimated distance of 750,000 light-years. Yet this distance had been arrived at by applying the period-luminosity law to cepheids found in the spiral, and in 1952 Baade reached the rather unhappy conclusion that all these had been assumed to be too faint. He showed that satisfactory agreement between magnitude and distance could be reached only by increasing their absolute magnitudes by 1·5 and by recognizing two types, each with its own period-luminosity law. Cepheids, like δ Cephei, which occupy the spiral arms of our Galaxy and of M31, are Type I cepheids of Population I. Those like the RR Lyrae stars are Type II cepheids of Population II, and are found in globular clusters and in great numbers in the nuclear regions of spiral galaxies. On this basis, and as previously noted on page 185, there are two period-luminosity curves separated in the main by a difference in absolute magnitude of about 1·5.

An increase in absolute magnitude of 1·5 means a four-fold increase in luminosity and therefore (by application of the Inverse

Nubecula minor – the Lesser Magellanic Cloud – a galaxy of irregular type. The network of 1° squares and the circle representing the moon indicate the apparent size of this galaxy in the southern sky.

Square Law of Illumination) a two-fold increase in distance. As a result of Baade's findings and suggestions, therefore, all distances ascertained by the observation of "classical" or Type I cepheids had to be increased by a factor of about two. The size of the universe was immediately doubled. M31, to give but one instance, was now assigned a distance of about 1,500,000 light-years, and twice the former linear size. This made it as large as our Galaxy, which had long seemed uniquely large.

Radial velocity studies of different parts of Messier 31 reveal that it is a rotating system. As in the case of our own Galaxy, it does not rotate as a solid wheel but at different rates at different distances from the center. Towards the center the angular rotation is approximately uniform or "wheel-like", but towards the edges it has planetary characteristics, decreasing with increasing distance from the center. The rotational period appears to be comparable to that of the Galaxy, as also is the mass, estimated at about 2×10^{11} suns and derived from considerations of the mode of rotation and the most likely distribution of material.

Prominent in southern skies and among neighbouring galaxies are the Magellanic Clouds. To the unaided eye they appear as two misty patches, and at their distance of some $30°$ to $45°$ from the galactic plane look like detached fragments of the Milky Way. Portuguese navigators in the fifteenth century called them the "Clouds of the Cape", but they were first described with reasonable accuracy by the chronicler of the expedition of Magellan in 1521. As photographed with large telescopes the Clouds are seen to be great complexes of millions of stars. They show no definite spiral structure and are generally classified as irregular galaxies.

Recent work has placed the Clouds at a distance of about 230,000 light-years. At this distance the sun would be too faint to be photographed: our knowledge of the stellar contents of the Clouds has therefore to be based on stars far more luminous than the sun, and in particular, on luminous cepheids and blue and red supergiants. The Large Cloud, roughly circular in outline, has a diameter of about 30,000 light-years. In it are found clusters of stars of the open galactic type, a few globular clusters, numerous EMISSION NEBULAE, and great quantities of interstellar dust. Among the stars is S Doradus, with a luminosity over 1,000,000 times that of the sun. Among the bright nebulae is the Tarantula Nebula, of 30 Doradus, a glowing mass of hydrogen gas so extensive that if it could be brought as near to us as the Orion Nebula it would extend across a quarter of the sky and give as much light as does the full moon.

To the naked eye and even with the telescope the Small Cloud is seen to occupy a fairly barren region of the sky. It is in the same part of the sky as the beautiful globular star cluster 47 Toucani (see page 198), but actually has no connection either with it or the Milky Way. Its size is just over half that of the Large Cloud and its contents are similar.

In experiments with a rapid "portrait" lens, H. C. RUSSELL in

1890 obtained photographs of the Large Clouds which hinted at a spiral structure. This feature has recently been followed up at Mount Stromlo Observatory, Australia, by Gérard de Vaucouleurs, who made a detailed photographic study of the outer regions of both Clouds. He suggests that they both carry signs of a type of galaxy called "barred spirals" in that arms originate from the ends of a main body, "axis" or "bar". This form is most apparent in the Great Cloud, where a long streamer is directed away from the Milky Way while another points towards it. De Vaucouleurs has also found traces of an extension of the Small Cloud in the direction of the Large Cloud, a feature strongly suggestive of tidal action. Studies of this kind can now draw on the resources of radio astronomy, particularly observations carried out at the 21 centimeter wavelength. In this field Frank J. KERR, and his associates Hindmann and Robinson of the Radiophysics Laboratory, Sydney, have not only mapped the distribution of neutral hydrogen on both Clouds but also determined the radial velocities of numerous areas in them. They find that while the Large Cloud is receding with respect to the Milky Way at an average rate of about 23 miles a second, the Small Cloud is approaching with a speed of 10 miles a second.

So great are the distances of the galaxies that the Magellanic Clouds can be regarded as very near neighbours of the Milky Way system and Messier 31 as a fairly near neighbour. Our Galaxy, in fact, is one of the largest members of a group of 14 galaxies which form the local group and which are all contained within a distance of about 2,000,000 light-years from us. In size Messier 31 is largest, the Galaxy is in second place, then comes the much smaller spiral Messier 33 in Triangulum with a diameter of about 38,000,000 light-years. At the lower end of the scale are comparatively small systems like Messier 32, one of the companions of Messier 31. This particular object is a good example of an ELLIPTICAL GALAXY, in that it is symmetrical, appears more condensed toward the center, and shows no signs whatever of spiral structure or associated dust clouds.

Once we move away from the members of the local cluster and the galaxies in its neighborhood, it is no longer possible to resolve

CLUSTER
NEBULA IN

RED-SHIFTS

VIRGO

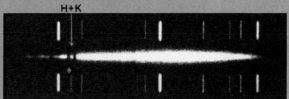

750 MILES PER SECOND

URSA MAJOR

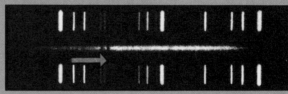

9,300 MILES PER SECOND

CORONA BOREALIS

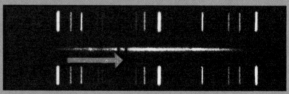

13,400 MILES PER SECOND

BOOTES

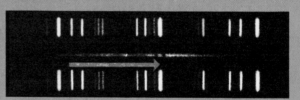

24,400 MILES PER SECOND

HYDRA

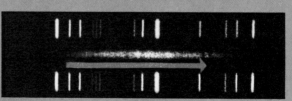

38,000 MILES PER SECOND

the remoter objects into individual stars, even with the 200-inch telescope. Hence we are forced to dispense with the clues provided by cepheids, novae and highly luminous stars in general, and must use other criteria for distance determination. An obvious choice is to assume that all galaxies have the same size and luminosity. A comparison of apparent sizes could then be interpreted directly in terms of distance, and objects too remote to present a measurable disk could have distances assigned to them on the basis of their apparent brightness. This method has been used with fair success in studies of the relative distances of large numbers of galaxies, but it takes no account of the fact that while some objects like Messier 31 are giants in both size and luminosity, others like Messier 32 are comparative dwarfs. Yet nearly every object in the immense variety of galaxies can be assigned to one of three main types – spiral, irregular and elliptical. Furthermore, nearly all small galaxies are elliptical and comparatively low in luminosity, the spirals are large and highly luminous, and the irregulars are intermediate in both size and luminosity. Advantage can therefore be taken of these trends in attempts to determine the distances of very remote galaxies, but only if they can be resolved into one of the three types.

Since the galaxies in the neighborhood of our own Galaxy form a local cluster, it is pertinent to ask whether more distant galaxies belong to groups and clusters. Many galaxies do, and the nearest are those which form a cluster in the constellation of Virgo, The Virgin. This cluster contains at least 500 members, most of them spirals. Among their number is the open spiral M100, whose distance Allan R. SANDAGE of the Mount Wilson and Palomar Observatories estimates to be 10,000,000 parsecs, or 325 million light-years. Also in this cluster is Messier 87, at a distance (according to Sandage) of approximately 13,000,000 parsecs, or 450,000,000 light-years. Another rich cluster is found in the constellation of Coma Berenices, near the north galactic pole. This contains up-

The velocity-distance relation for galaxies. The tip of the red arrow in each spectrum lies just below the H and K lines of calcium. The length of the arrow indicates the amounts these lines are displaced towards the red.

The spiral nebula in Virgo (Messier 104) seen edge on, through the 200-inch Hale telescope. Some of the globular clusters surrounding this galaxy are indicated thus–·–

wards of 800 individuals at a mean distance of about 100,000,000 light-years. And yet these two, along with the local cluster, are but three of the large number of clusters of galaxies. As a result of a recent photographic survey made with the 48-inch Palomar Schmidt telescope, G. O. Abell has been able to form a catalogue of no less than 2712 rich clusters of galaxies. These may, in turn, be associated in groups to form super-clusters, the largest units of the observable domain.

A few galaxies have been found to be strong sources of radio waves. In 1950, R. Hanbury Brown and Cyril Hazard, working at a frequency of 158·5 megacycles per second with the great 218-foot paraboloidal aerial at Jodrell Bank, near Manchester, England, detected radiation from Messier 31. Many other galaxies and groups of galaxies have since been detected by this and similar means, but all of them are extremely weak radio sources. Radio investigations have now revealed large numbers of discrete or localized sources of radio energy, formerly called "radio stars".

Only a few, however, have been identified with optical objects: the remainder have as yet no optical counterparts, although some astronomers consider that these will one day be found to coincide with faint galaxies.

Three of the radio sources, like the intense one in Taurus, have been identified with galactic supernovae remnants. Others, like Cassiopeia A (the most intense radio source in the sky), are known to be associated with extremely faint filamentary nebulosities. But one particularly strong one, Cygnus A, occupies the same position as an object which, on photographs taken with the 200-inch telescope, looks like two galaxies in collision. Their distance is well over 100,000,000 parsecs and the collision velocity is estimated to be about 25,000 miles a second. If this is indeed the source, the radio waves would arise more from the collision of interstellar material in the galaxies than from any chance collision of one star with another. Another fairly strong source, Centaurus A, has also been identified with a peculiar looking object in a cluster of galaxies which the 200-inch telescope resolves into two apparently colliding galaxies. Weak sources in Perseus and Hydra are also associated with colliding galaxies, and one in Virgo, Virgo A, has been identified with a disk-shaped galaxy from which

A cluster of nebulae in Coma Berenices, as seen through the 200-inch Hale telescope.

protrudes a streak of gaseous material nearly 2000 light-years long. Yet lest it be thought that colliding galaxies always constitute strong radio sources, all attempts have so far failed to locate radio sources in the positions of two colliding systems, NGC 1487 and NGC 3256.

When we consider the immense distances which separate the galaxies in the local cluster, collisions and even close approaches must be more the exception than the rule. In some rich clusters of galaxies, however, the individuals appear to be quite closely packed, and then it is that collisions can take place and even be fairly frequent over many millions of years. Close approaches are also possible, and evidence for these has already been found by Fritz ZWICKY in the form of luminous "bridges" which appear to connect neighboring galaxies. All this means that galaxies are *moving* objects – that they are moving relative to each other and to our own Galaxy. The only detectable component of their space motion, however, is the radial velocity, and for this the spectrograph has yielded some extremely remarkable results.

The radial velocity of a galaxy was measured for the first time in 1912 by Vesto SLIPHER at the Lowell Observatory. He found that the H and K lines of calcium in the spectrum of Messier 31 showed a slight shift towards the violet, and assuming this to be a Doppler-Fizeau effect, concluded that the velocity of approach is about 190 miles a second. By 1925, Slipher had secured the radial velocities of 41 galaxies, most of them positive or directed away from the observer. They ranged from minus 190 miles a second to plus 1125 miles a second, and were then regarded as being exceptionally large. Even more surprising were the results obtained in 1929. E. P. Hubble of the Mount Wilson Observatory had by then succeeded in securing the distances of these galaxies, reasoning that statistically the relative brightnesses of galaxies could be taken as the measure of their distances. He showed that the velocities, corrected for the effect of the sun's velocity around the Galactic center, were not only all positive but also increased in direct proportion to the distance of the observed galaxy. Milton L. HUMASON confirmed this a year later, and by means of a high-speed spectrograph attached to the 100-inch telescope, was able to extend Hubble's linear velocity/distance relationship to a galaxy at a distance of 240,000,000 light-years. The shift of the lines towards the red became known as the RED SHIFT, and the linear relationship came to be regarded as a general characteristic of the observable region itself.

Subsequent work has fully confirmed this supposition. In 1936 Humason reached the limit of the 100-inch telescope when he obtained a spectrogram of a galaxy in a cluster in Ursa Major which showed a velocity of recession of 25,000 miles a second, or about one-eighth the velocity of light. All the way out to this distance of about 500,000,000 light-years the velocity increased as Hubble had predicted – in direct proportion with the distance. Then came the 200-inch telescope, whose immense light-grasp enabled spectrograms to be taken of objects so remote that the red-shift corresponds to a velocity of 38,000 miles a second and suggests a distance of about 800,000,000 light-years.

If the red-shifts are interpreted as Doppler-Fizeau effects, it is clear that the galaxies are all receding from our own Galaxy and from each other. This interpretation has given rise to the notion that the universe is expanding. While everything appears to be in favour of the red-shifts being due to velocities of recession, there is still the alternative that they represent some hitherto unrecognized principle in physics. It is also pertinent to ask: "what exactly is expanding – the universe of motion, the space in it, or the distances between galaxies and clusters of galaxies"? "Space," "motion" and "distance" are all concepts rather than things which the astronomer has somehow to measure. They are, moreover, concepts definable only within the range of actual experience, and as such can be provided with whatever attributes we choose to give them. Yet if we overlook these philosophical considerations we have, apparently, a system whose state is not one of quiescence but of expansion. We can infer that the universe is finite in both space and time. If the rate of expansion is assumed to have been always the same, all the observed galaxies were once crowded in the same space and presumably had a common origin. According to Canon Georges LEMAÎTRE, at some distant time in the past, recently estimated to be about 5000 million years ago, an enormous primeval "atom" exploded to form units having masses which were comparable with those of the galaxies in the observable domain.

Since the galaxies appear to be all running away from each other, the time will come when every one of them should be beyond the range of observation. An astronomer looking out into space many billions of years hence would therefore conclude that the Galaxy alone constitutes the observable domain. According to a recent theory, however, this would not arise, for the universe is infinite in both space and time. As galaxies pass beyond the range of observation so they will be replaced by others formed by the continuous creation of matter. The mean density of the universe is therefore in a "steady-state" and the galaxies should be of all ages. If, on the other hand, the universe had a beginning in time and the mean density is progressively decreasing, the more distant a galaxy the younger its age should be. At present there is no way of deciding one way or the other, and only one thing remains sure – the red shifts so far observed in spectrograms of galaxies accessible to the 200-inch telescope are directly proportional to the apparent brightness of those galaxies.

Just over half a century ago the sun was still regarded as having a fairly central position in the universe. The latter, however, was a far smaller affair than the one revealed by modern astronomy, for its limits were none other than those of our own Milky Way system. The distinguished American astronomer Simon Newcomb expressed the general opinion about this in 1906, when he wrote: "The universe, so far as we can see it, is a bounded whole. It is surrounded by an immense girdle of stars, which to our vision, appears as the Milky Way." Its diameter, Newcomb suggested, is probably about 6600 light-years, and he expressed the hope that "astronomers, through coming centuries, will obtain a little more light on the subject – will be enabled to make more definite boundaries of our system of stars, and to draw more and more probable conclusions as to the existence or non-existence of any object outside of it."

Today, as we have already seen, the sun has been relegated to a position in a spiral arm about two-thirds of the way out from the center of the Galaxy. This Galaxy, moreover, with an overall diameter of about 100,000 light-years, is by no means the largest or the only one of its type. The 200-inch telescope reaches out to more than 2000 million light-years (large radio telescopes may take us even further), and therefore covers a region which, according to Shapley, contains about 2000 million galaxies. Our Galaxy is not at the center of the universe. Furthermore what an observer sees does not depend upon his position. If we could, for example, survey the universe of galaxies from a planet in an extremely remote galaxy, its overall aspect would be similar to the one we already observe. Other galaxies would still appear to be all running away from us, and their large-scale distribution would still appear to be uniform.

Since the sun is but one unit among tens of billions of stars in the Galaxy, how much more insignificant is it in relation to the whole! In the great domain of the galaxies the earth, with a volume only about one-millionth that of the sun, is even more insignificant, a mere speck in the vast ocean of space and time. Small wonder, therefore, that some scientists regard life as a kind of accident and man as a by-product on a grain of dust. A by-product, moreover, whose entire history since the dawn of civilization has been no longer than a tick of the astronomer's clock.

The age of the earth, as estimated from studies of radio-active decay in rocks, appears to be of the order of four billion years, a figure compatible with the likely age of the sun. At its present rate of energy radiation, and if the amount of helium present has arisen from the conversion of hydrogen into helium by the carbon cycle and proton-proton reaction, the sun's age must be not less than three billion years. This figure is also of the same order as that obtained for what is often called the "age" of the universe. As we have already seen (page 233), if we assume that the red shift represents motion, the galaxies at their present rate of recession would all have had a common origin about five billion years ago. All these time intervals are, of course, purely tentative. They must on no account be regarded as a "date of Creation", but they do give some idea at least of the immense length of the astronomical time-scale.

Any ideas we may form about the mode of origin of the earth and other planets must likewise be highly conjectural: we have necessarily left the findings of observation for the uncertainties of speculation. Some theories have suggested that the planets may have been formed as a result of the sun's close encounter with another star or stars. Immense tides were produced in the sun, and streams of incandescent material poured forth like gigantic prominences. This material, by reason of the sun's rotation and the relative motion of the two stars, then formed spiral arms around the sun. From the larger condensations in these arms came the major planets, and from the smaller, attracted into the vicinity of the larger, came the satellites. Alternatively, the solar system may have developed from a cloud of dust and gas, with local irregularities gradually producing rotation and forming centers of attraction which ultimately became the planets. Perhaps the sun and stars had their origins in a similar way, having condensed out of the primeval undifferentiated chaos of universal gas and dust. But since the stars differ in physical characteristics, so doubtless they differ in age, and it may well be that the dark reaches of interstellar material form the mother-stuff from which stars are still being born.

If planets come into existence only as the result of stellar encounters, the number of planetary systems must be very small compared with the number of stars. The stars are separated from each other by tremendous distances, and astronomers have yet to observe a stellar flare-up which can be described in terms of a pair of colliding stars. Sir James JEANS, the famous British cosmologist, thought that only one star in a million may be surrounded by planets: hence there should be about 100,000 planetary systems in the Galaxy. In 1950, Fred HOYLE wrote that the Galaxy in the past must have had nearly 10,000,000 planetary systems, but in 1955 he revised the number to 100 billion. Yet Sir Harold SPENCER JONES gave the view in 1952 that the number of planetary systems in the Galaxy is not likely to be more than several hundred. These discrepancies reveal just how little reliance can be placed on the statements of cosmologists when they deal with problems so greatly removed from observation.

So great are the distances of the stars that planets as large as and larger than Jupiter could not possibly be detected by direct optical means. There are a few cases, however, where the apparent motion of a star has irregularities which suggest the perturbing influence of a dark companion of planetary dimensions. The reader will recall that Struve predicted the Companion of Sirius as a result of observations of the sinuous motion of Sirius itself (page 178). In recent years a similar motion has been found in the motions of the components of a few binary stars, among them 61 Cygni, but the perturbing bodies themselves are quite invisible even in the most powerful telescopes.

Within the limitations of modern observation, therefore, the earth is the only planet in the universe capable of supporting highly developed forms of life. The question whether similar forms of life exist elsewhere than on the earth is not a legitimate scientific question at all – not, at least, until it can be tested either by direct or indirect observation. Some writers seem to regard it as a necessary corollary of faith to suppose that the Creator has set inhabitants on all the worlds. The purpose of so many stars and systems of stars, they think, is not merely to add interest to the night sky, but to enable intelligent life to gain as many footholds as possible. Some point to the prodigality of nature, suggesting that it is in the nature of things for many stars to be formed so that only one may have around it a system of planets. Others consider life to be no more than a freak brought about in the first place by an accidental combination of elements. Yet despite all these and other differences in viewpoint, one thing is clear: that although in point of size man is utterly insignificant, he has moral and spiritual qualities which enable him completely to transcend the material universe. He knows. He is at home in and with the universe. He can measure and weigh the stars, count them in their millions, and in imagination follow them in their journeyings in space and time.

Man's questing spirit recognizes no physical boundaries, and he is now preparing to travel to regions far beyond the earth. The first step towards realizing this ambition was the post-war exploration of the upper atmosphere by rocket soundings. Fired to reach maximum heights of several hundred miles, research rockets carried instruments which TELEMETERED back to ground information about cosmic ray intensities, ultra-violet radiation, ionization, magnetic field, and the pressure, density and temperature of the air. In 1953 E. L. Singer suggested that this work could be supplemented by arranging for a small artificial satellite to orbit the earth at a height of about 300 miles above the surface. At this height, and with an initial period of approximately 90 minutes, a satellite would make many revolutions before the cumulative effect of air drag causes it to move low enough to be vaporized and end its useful life as a bright meteor. Throughout this time, instruments in the satellite could continuously transmit information to ground stations.

On October 4, 1957, and as part of the activities of the International Geophysical Year (IGY), the Soviet Union successfully launched Sputnik I, the first artificial earth satellite. This took the form of an instrumented aluminum-alloy sphere nearly 23 inches in diameter and weighing about 184 pounds. At an initial mean height of 560 miles and approximate speed of 18,000 miles an hour, Sputnik I, together with the rocket nose-cone and empty case of the third-stage rocket, orbited the earth once every 96 minutes. Thereafter, and owing to air resistance, the mean height and speed decreased, and after about 96 days all three objects had disintegrated in the denser layers of the earth's atmosphere. A second Soviet earth satellite, Sputnik II, containing instruments and a dog, Laika, and having a total weight reputed to be nearly half a ton, went into orbit on November 3, 1957. This second Soviet achievement was soon followed by the launching of a large modified Jupiter-C missile from Cape Canaveral, Florida. On January 31, 1958, Explorer I, a pencil-shaped satellite 80 inches long was in orbit, travelling around the earth in a period just a few minutes short of two hours.

Since then, and in addition to the successful launching of other artificial satellites, three small space probes are in orbit around the sun. This means that small bodies can now be given an initial velocity of at least 25,000 miles an hour, for at this velocity they can escape completely from the earth. The first space probe passed within 4,500 miles of the moon and is called Mechta, or Artificial Planet I. Launched on January 2, 1959, from a site in the U.S.S.R., Mechta moved into a 443-day period orbit which carried it at perihelion to 91,000,000 miles from the sun, and at aphelion to a distance of just over 122,000,000 miles. The second artificial planet, Pioneer IV, was launched from Cape Canaveral on March 3, 1959. This cone-shaped probe measured 21 inches from base to apex and 22 inches across the base. Made of fiberglass, it was gold-plated so that the shell could act as a radio aerial, and black-striped to increase heat absorption. 41 hours after take-off it passed within 37,000 miles of the moon and was tracked by radio telescopes to a distance of 400,000 miles. Both Mechta and Pioneer IV are no longer transmitting signals, and there is no likelihood that they will ever be picked up again.

Pioneer V, the third artificial planet, was launched from Cape Canaveral on March 11, 1960. Its path lies between those of the earth and Venus, although at no time can it go closer to Venus or the orbit of Venus than about 7,000,000 miles. In response to a signal from the earth, Pioneer V can transmit its information over a distance of many million miles. At the time of writing it is hoped that this transmission will be possible for about half of the period of orbital revolution of 311 days.

Artificial satellites and space probes can be equipped with a wide variety of instruments to measure, among other things, the earth's magnetic field, intensity of radiation and cosmic rays, temperature within the vehicle, and frequency of encounter with micrometeorites. From instruments carried in the American Explorer satellites we now know that above about 500 miles from the surface the earth is surrounded by a zone or zones of radiation. This is known as the VAN ALLEN RADIATION BELT, after J. A. Van Allen who has been in charge of cosmic ray experiments with American artificial satellites and space probes. Pioneer IV also provided further information about this belt and indicated that the radiation is still quite intense at a distance of about 10,000 miles from the earth. It began its flight just after a period of intense solar activity, and the results of its measurements of the radiation levels indicate that at least the outer radiation zone is of solar origin.

Lunik II, the first man-made object to reach the moon, was

launched on September 13, 1959. After a flight of only 35 hours, both the 860-pound instrument probe and 3331-pound final-stage rocket crashed on the moon's surface. On October 4 in the same year, as we mentioned in Chapter 4, Lunik III orbited the moon and transmitted back the first pictures of its far side. Similar probes could also be used for the initial explorations of Mercury, Venus and Mars, and the great planets beyond.

In view of recent achievements we can be sure that the next decade will see developments equally remarkable. The United States in particular is committed to a number of intensive and ambitious space projects, all of them stages towards the ultimate goal of manned space-travel. Having achieved this goal, what will be its value as far as astronomy is concerned? It will, for sure, make possible journeys to the moon and planets, thereby enabling us to make closer surveys of their features and even, in some cases, actual physical contact with their surfaces. For these purposes the moon will provide an excellent "proving ground", and it may be possible to establish permanent bases there. It is certain that if an observatory could be set up on the moon, or on an artificial satellite large enough to act as a "space station", it would be able to penetrate much further into space as it would be unhampered by atmospheric effects.

Artificial earth satellites, space probes, and lunar probes are all necessary stages in the physical conquest of space, and all are in the first process of development. In principle they could be developed to act as so many distant hands and eyes – the artificial satellites to become remotely controllable space laboratories and astronomical observatories, and the lunar probes, mobile vehicles capable of being directed over the moon's surface. But there may come a stage at which the complexity of the machine to do the job becomes intolerable. In the words of the earth-satellite technical panel of the United States National Committee for the IGY, "a man is found to be more efficient, more reliable, and above all more resourceful when unexpected obstacles arise. It is, in a sense, an article of faith that man will indeed be required to do the job of cosmic exploration personally – and, furthermore, that he will *want* to do the job himself, whether required to or not".

Glossary

Absolute magnitude. The magnitude which a star would have when moved to a distance of 10 parsecs or 32·6 light-years. Its parallax would then be 0·1 seconds of arc.

Achromatic lens. A lens which produces optical images free from false color.

Adams, Walter S. American astronomer (1876–1956). Specialized in stellar spectroscopy at the Yerkes and Mount Wilson Observatories.

Ahnighito. "The Tent". The name of a large meteorite preserved in the American Museum–Hayden Planetarium, New York City.

Airy disk. The false or spurious disk which a first-class object-glass forms for the image of a star.

Almagest. The contracted Arabic name of a great encyclopedia of astronomy written by Claudius Ptolemy, an astronomer of the 2nd century A.D.

Annular eclipse. An eclipse of the sun in which the moon does not completely cover the sun but leaves a ring or annulus of the sun's disk around the darkened moon.

Anode. The positive pole of an electrical current.

Antapex. The point on the celestial sphere from which the sun and entire solar system is retreating at about 12 miles a second.

Aphelion. The point on the orbit of a planet or comet which is farthest from the sun.

Apogee. The point on the orbit of the moon or artificial earth satellite which is farthest from the earth.

Apsides, line of. The greater axis of an elliptical orbit, and therefore the line which passes through the two foci.

Aristarchus. Greek astronomer of the first half of the 3rd century B.C. Made estimates of the distances of the sun and moon and held that the earth not only rotated on its axis, but moved round the sun.

Asterism. A group of stars which may or may not form a constellation. The stars of The Big Dipper, for example, form an asterism in the constellation of The Great Bear.

Asteroid. A member of a group of small planets, "planetoids" or "minor planets" which move round the sun. In the main their orbits lie between those of Mars and Jupiter.

Astronomical spectrograph. An instrument for obtaining photographs of the spectra of celestial objects.

Astrophysics. The study of the physics and chemistry of celestial objects.

Atom. The smallest unit of an element which can take part in a chemical reaction.

Baade, Walter F. American astronomer at the Mount Wilson and Palomar Observatories. Noted for his observational work on galactic and extragalactic objects and for introducing the concept of two types of stellar populations.

Baily's beads. A bead-like line of light seen during a total solar eclipse on the sun's limb immediately before and after totality. So-called after Francis Baily, an English astronomer who described them in 1836.

Barnard, Edward E. American astronomer (1857–1923). Produced in 1927 a celebrated photographic "Atlas of Selected Regions of the Milky Way".

Bayer, Johann. German lawyer (1572–1625). Published in 1603 the *Uranometria*, a fine star atlas which went through several editions.

Bessel, Friedrich W. German astronomer (1784–1846). Director of the Königsberg Observatory. Published in 1818 a catalogue of the places of 3222 stars. Made the first definite estimate of the parallax of a star (61 Cygni).

Binoculars. A pair of telescopes, optically equivalent, arranged in parallel for use with both eyes.

Biot, Jean-B. French physicist and astronomer (1774–1862).

Bode, Johann E. German astronomer (1747–1826). Usually regarded as the author of Bode's Law, but this was first suggested by Titius of Wittenberg. Published a large star atlas in 1801.

Bode's law. An empirical law connecting the distances of the planets from the sun. The law is: To each of the series of numbers 0, 3, 6, 12, 24, 48, 96, 192, 384, add 4. We then obtain the series 4, 7, 10, 16, 28, 52, 100, 196 and 388, which represents approximately the distances of the planets from the sun—with the exception of Neptune.

Bradley, James. English astronomer (1693–1762). 3rd Astronomer Royal. Discovered the aberration of light and nutation.

Calver, George. An English manufacturer of reflecting telescopes in the late 19th century.

Carbon cycle. A six-stage series of thermonuclear reactions which begin by the nucleus of a carbon atom capturing a hydrogen nucleus or proton. The complete process releases an immense amount of energy.

Campbell, William. American astrophysicist (1862–1938). Director of the Lick Observatory (1900–1938).

Carpenter, James. English astronomer (1840–1899).

Carrington, Richard. English amateur astronomer 1826–1875). His observations of sunspots led to the first clear recognition of the difference in the rate of rotation of different parts of the surface of the sun.

Cassegrain, Guillaume. Inventor of the Cassegrain reflecting telescope, news of which first came to England in 1672.

Cassini, Giovanni D. Italian astronomer (1625–1712). An eminent planetary observer and first director of the Paris Observatory.

Cassini division. The dark space or gap between the outer ring of Saturn and the bright inner ring. It was first seen by G. D. Cassini in 1675.

Catalyst. Any substance that changes the speed of a chemical reaction without itself being changed.

Cathode. The negative pole of an electrical current.

Celestial equator. The great circle in which the plane of the earth's equator meets the celestial sphere.

Celestial poles. The two points in which the earth's axis meets the celestial sphere.

Celestial sphere. The great sphere of the heavens, once thought to surround the earth and to be made of transparent material in which the stars were embedded. The idea is still retained for convenience in fixing the positions of celestial objects.

Centigrade. A uniform scale of temperature on which the temperature of melting ice is 0 degrees and that of boiling water (at normal atmospheric pressure) is 100 degrees.

Cepheids. Variable stars whose characteristics in light behavior are similar to those of the prototype Delta Cephei.

Chladni, Ernst F. F. German physicist (1756–1827). Studied the vibrations of strings, rods and plates and made a collection of meteorites.

Chromatic aberration. The defect of an uncorrected lens or system of lenses in failing to bring light of all colours to one and the same focus.

Chromosphere. The name given to that part of the sun's atmosphere from which the prominences rise. It shines with a rosy light and is composed mainly of hydrogen gas.

Clark, Alvan G. and Sons. An American firm of opticians famous for the manufacture of large refractors, including the object-glasses of the 36-inch Lick and 40-inch Yerkes Observatories.

Clepsydra. An early device for showing time based on the uniform rate of flow of water, oil or sand through a small hole or pipe.

Cluster type variables. Variable stars with RR Lyrae as their prototype and so called because they were first discovered in globular clusters.

Coefficient of expansion. The increase of volume for a rise in temperature of 1°C. expressed as a decimal fraction of the volume at 0°C.

Collimating lens. A lens which gives parallel rays of light by having a target or light-source at its focus.

Color excess. The reddening of distant stars owing to the scattering of their light by interstellar material.

Coma. (1) The defect of a lens or lens system in which star images appear pear-shaped. (2) The hazy region round the nucleus of a comet.

Comet. A body which often develops a hair-like appendage and moves round the sun usually in a highly elongated orbit.

Constellations. The groups or patterns into which the stars were divided in ancient times presumably to assist identification.

Copernicus, Nicholas. Polish astronomer (1473–1543). Taught that the earth is spherical, rotates on its axis and revolves round the sun; also that the motions of the heavenly bodies are either circular and uniform or compounded of circular and uniform motions.

Corona. The halo of relatively faint light surrounding the sun. It can be seen by the unaided eye only at the time of a total solar eclipse.

Coronagraph. An instrument which brings about an artificial total eclipse of the sun and makes possible the direct study of the corona.

Cosmogony. The investigation of the origin of the physical universe.

Cosmologist. A person who investigates the laws and structure of the physical universe.

Cosmos. The physical universe.

Crater (Lunar). A shallow circular feature on the moon's surface some 3 miles to 30 miles in diameter. Many craters possess a central mountain peak.

Craterlet (Lunar). A small crater on the moon's surface ranging in diameter from a few feet to 2 to 3 miles.

D-layer. The lowest layer of the ionosphere.

Declination. The angular distance of a heavenly body north or south of the celestial equator. It is measured on a great circle passing through the body and the celestial poles.

Deferent. The circular path along which moved the center of a planetary epicycle in the Ptolemaic system of the universe.

Degree. A unit of angular measure, there being 360 degrees in a complete circle.

Delporte, Eugène J. Belgian astronomer (1882–1955). Director of the Belgian Royal Observatory. Specialized in determining the positions of asteroids and comets.

Diffraction. The deflection of light when it passes the edges of obstacles placed in its path.

Digges, Leonard. A 16th-century English mathematician who had advanced ideas (for his time) about optics and astronomy.

Digges, Thomas. Elizabethan scientist, the son of Leonard Digges.

Dollond, John. London master-optician (1706–1761). Famous for the manufacture of the first achromatic telescopes.

Dollond, Peter. London master-optician (1730–1820). Son of John Dollond.

Doppler, Christian. Austrian physicist (1803–1853).

Doppler-Fizeau shifts. The displacement of Fraunhofer lines in the spectra of luminous objects due to their relative motion towards or away from the observer.

Draper, Henry. American astronomer (1837–1882). Constructed his own reflecting telescopes and established a private observatory at Hastings-on-Hudson. Pioneered in the photography of stellar spectra.

Earthshine. The dark part of the moon made visible slightly before and slightly after the time of new moon by sunlight reflected from the earth.

Eccentricity of an orbit. The distance of each of the foci from the center of the ellipse expressed as a decimal fraction of the semi-major axis.

Eclipse. The passing of one celestial body through the shadow of another. The term is also applied to the sun when its light is partly or completely cut off by the moon.

Eclipsing binary. A pair of stars, physically connected and moving in orbits so orientated with respect to the observer that one star periodically eclipses its companion. Also called an "eclipsing variable".

Ecliptic. A great circle of the celestial sphere along which the sun apparently travels during a year.

Eddington, Sir Arthur S. English astrophysicist (1882–1944). Plumian Professor of Astronomy in the University of Cambridge, and Director of the Cambridge Observatory.

Einstein, Albert. German scientist (1879–1955). Founder of the theory of relativity and a great pioneer in mathematical physics.

Einstein effect. The effect produced by the deflection of light when it traverses a gravitational field as predicted by Einstein's theory of relativity.

Electromagnetic energy. Terms descriptive of the radiation received from the sun and stars, denoting that it can be regarded as a form of energy with electrical and magnetic properties.

Electromagnetic spectrum. The entire range of electromagnetic energy in terms of wavelength and frequency when spread out in a spectrum.

Electron. A unit negative charge of electricity to which is ascribed the property of mass.

Ellipse. A conic section formed by the intersection of a plane with a cone, the plane being inclined to the axis of the cone and cutting the sides of the cone.

Ellipsoid. The surface generated by a variable ellipse whose center moves along a line drawn perpendicular to its axis.

Elliptical galaxies. Galaxies or systems of stars which have an elliptical appearance and reveal no trace of spiral structure.

Elongation. The apparent angular distance of a body from its parent, as of Mercury and Venus from the sun, or a satellite from its planet.

Emission nebula. Interstellar gas excited into luminescence by extremely hot stars embedded in it. The gas gives rise to a bright-line or emission spectrum.

Eon. An immense period of time.

Epicycle. In the Ptolemaic system of the universe, the comparatively small circular path of a planet, the center of which moved on the circumference of a larger circle called the "deferent".

Equal areas, Law of. Kepler's second law of planetary motion which states that as a planet moves round the sun, a line joining it to the sun sweeps out equal areas in equal times.

Equinoctial hours. Hours of equal length, whether reckoned by day or by night.

Equinox. Either of the two points at which the sun, in its apparent annual path against the starry background, crosses the celestial equator. These points are therefore those where the ecliptic intersects the celestial equator.

Eratosthenes. Greek scholar and astronomer, 3rd century B.C. Chief Librarian at the Museum Library, Alexandria. A pioneer in cartography and the first to measure the diameter of the earth by an astronomical method.

Extra-galactic nebula. An immense system of stars or "galaxy" independent of the Milky Way system of which the sun is a member.

Fabricius, David. Frisian clergyman. First to detect in 1596 the variability of Mira Ceti.

Faculae. Latin for "torches". Parts of the sun's surface brighter than the general level of intensity of the photosphere and usually found near sunspots.

First point of Aries. The point on the celestial equator reached by the sun at the time of the vernal equinox. Owing to the precession of the equinoxes, this point is now no longer in the constellation of Aries but in that of Pisces.

First quarter. The phase of the moon when it has completed one quarter of one complete revolution round the earth, relative to the sun. It then appears as a half moon in the evening sky.

Fixed stars. So distant are the stars that naked-eye observations of them over many years fails to reveal any changes in their relative positions. They therefore appear to be fixed in the heavens.

Fizeau, Armand Hippolyte Louis. French physicist

(1819–1896). Made in 1849 the earliest experimental determination of the velocity of light.

Flamsteed, John. English astronomer (1646–1719). First Astronomer Royal at the Royal Greenwich Observatory. Prepared a fine atlas of the northern stars.

Flares, Solar. Extremely intense and localized eruptions on the sun which interfere with radio, telephone and telegraphic communication.

Flash spectrum. The bright-line or emission spectrum which can be observed for a few seconds at the beginning and end of a total solar eclipse.

Fluorescence. The property of certain substances of absorbing energy of short wavelength and emitting it at longer wavelength.

Focal length. For a single mirror or thin lens, the distance measured along its optical axis from the centre of its surface to the focus.

Focus. The point to which light and heat are reflected by a concave mirror or refracted by a convex lens.

Foucault, Jean Bernard Léon. French physicist (1819–1868). Made experimental determinations of the velocity of light in air and water. Demonstrated the rotation of the earth by means of the pendulum.

Fraunhofer, Joseph von. German physicist and optician (1787–1826). Drew attention to the dark lines in absorption spectra and perfected the refracting telescope.

Fraunhofer lines. Dark lines named after Fraunhofer and seen in the spectra of the sun, moon, stars and planets. They are due to the selective absorption of radiation.

Flocculi. Bright and dark patches on the surface of the sun revealed by photographs taken in monochromatic light.

Galactic clusters *see* **Open star clusters.**

Galactic plane. A plane perpendicular to the line joining the galactic poles and located midway between them. It meets the Milky Way about 1° north of the center line of the Milky Way.

Galactic poles. The two opposite points that are farthest north and south of the Milky Way.

Galaxy. An immense system of stars, star clusters, nebulae, gas and dust, independent from and similar to the Milky Way System of which the sun is a member.

Galaxy, The *see* **Milky Way System.**

Galilei, Galileo. Italian mathematician and physicist (1564–1642). Established the science of moving bodies and was the first to use the telescope for astronomical observation.

Gauss, Johann K. F. German mathematician (1777–1855). Pioneered in the computation of planetary orbits.

Geocentric. As seen from or referred to the center of the earth.

Gibbous. An adjective applied to the apparent shape of the moon or a planet when more than half but less than the whole illuminated area is visible.

Globular star cluster. A Compact cluster or swarm of stars having an overall spherical or near spherical form.

Goodricke, John. English amateur astronomer (1764–1786). First to detect the regularity of the light changes of the stars Algol and Beta Lyrae.

Gravitation, Law of. First enunciated by Sir Isaac Newton. It states that: "All bodies tend to attract one another with a force proportional to the product of their masses and inversely proportional to the square of the distance between them".

Great circle. The circle on a sphere whose plane passes through the center of the sphere.

Great red spot. A conspicuous and oval-shaped reddish spot which appeared on the planet Jupiter in 1898 and is still visible, although to a much less marked degree.

Gregorian Calendar. The calendar as used today and as introduced by Pope Gregory XIII in 1582. Every year which is a multiple of 100 and is divisible by 400 is a leap year, and those not divisible by 400 are not leap years.

Gregory, James. Scottish mathematician (1638–1675). Proposed in 1663 the Gregorian form of reflecting telescope.

Gruithuisen, Franz von. Bavarian astronomer (1774–1852). Professor of astronomy at Munich. Advanced the meteoric theory of the formation of the craters on the moon.

Hale, George E. American astronomer (1868–1938). Took a prominent part in the foundation of the Yerkes, Mount Wilson and Palomar Observatories. Invented the spectroheliograph and spectrohelioscope.

Hall, Asaph. American astronomer (1829–1907). Director of the Naval Observatory, Washington. Discovered the two satellites of Mars.

Hall, Chester Moor. A London barrister and amateur optician. Invented the achromatic telescope about 1729.

Halley, Edmond. English astronomer (1656–1742). Second Astronomer-Royal. Published in 1678 a catalogue of the places of 341 southern stars. Investigated terrestrial magnetism and predicted the 1759 return of the comet named after him.

Harvest moon. The full moon which falls on or nearest to the date of the autumnal equinox.

Hencke, Karl L. German amateur astronomer (1793–1866). Discovered Astraea, the fifth asteroid, after a search of 15 years.

Herschel, Sir John F. W. English astronomer (1792–1871). Son of Sir William Herschel. Made an expedition to the Cape of Good Hope (1833–1838) in order to study southern skies.

Herschel, Sir William. German astronomer (1738–1822). Spent most of his life in England where he made several surveys of the heavens with large reflecting telescopes of his own construction. Discovered the planet Uranus in 1781.

Hertzsprung-Russell diagram. The diagram obtained by plotting the absolute magnitudes of stars against their spectral types.

Hevelius, Johann. Danish astronomer (1611–1687). Published in 1647 his *Selenographia*, or description of the chief surface features of the moon.

Hipparchus. Greek astronomer of the 2nd century B.C. Made an extensive series of observations with graduated instruments. Re-discovered the precession of the equinoxes and laid down the geometrical framework of the Ptolemaic system.

Hour circle. Any great circle on the celestial sphere which passes through both the celestial poles.

Hoyle, Fred. Plumian Professor of astronomy and experimental philosophy in the University of Cambridge, England.

Hubble, Edwin P. American astronomer and cosmologist (1889–1953). Associated with the Mount Wilson Observatory from 1919 until his death. Noted for his work on galaxies.

Huggins, Sir William. English astronomer (1824–1910). Pioneered in astrophysics and was the first to obtain the spectrum of a gaseous nebula.

Humason, Milton L. Formerly astronomer at the Mount Wilson and Palomar Observatories. Noted for his work on the radial velocities of galaxies.

Huygens, Christian. Dutch scientist (1629–1695). An early exponent of the wave theory of light and a pioneer in the science of dynamics. Discovered the rings of Saturn.

Hydrogen chain *see* **Proton-proton reaction.**

Hyperbola. A conic section formed by the intersection of a plane with a cone, the plane being perpendicular to the base of the cone.

Hyperboloid. The surface generated by rotating a hyperbola around its axis.

Inertia, Law of. Newton's First Law of Motion which states that: "Every body perseveres in its state of rest or of uniform motion in a straight line except in so far as it is made to change that state by external forces".

Inferior conjunction. The position of either of the two planets Mercury and Venus when they pass between or nearly between the earth and the sun.

Infra-red. A section of the electromagnetic spectrum lying just beyond the red and therefore invisible to the human eye.

Interstellar dust. Vast expanses of tiny particles which occupy the regions between the stars.

Interstellar lines. Fraunhofer lines superimposed on the spectrum of a star by reason of the selective absorption of radiation by interstellar gas somewhere between the star and the earth.

Inverse square law of illumination. The law which states that the intensity of illumination of a point source varies inversely as the square of the distance from the source.

Ion. An electrified particle formed when an atom loses or gains one or more electrons.

Ionosphere. A layer of ionized air high up in the earth's atmosphere.

Irregular nebula. A diffuse and generally chaotic mass of luminous gas usually associated with interstellar dust.

Janssen, Pierre J. C. French astronomer (1824–1907). Pioneered in solar spectroscopy.

Jeans, Sir James H. English mathematician and astronomer (1877–1946). Noted for his speculations in cosmogony and writings on astronomy.

Julian Calendar. The calendar introduced in B.C. 44 by Julius Caesar in which one year in every four is a leap year.

Kant, Immanuel. German philosopher (1724–1804). Speculated about the construction of the physical universe, believing it to be made up of individual nebulae or "island universes".

Kapteyn, Jacobus C. Dutch astronomer (1851–1922). Pioneered in stellar statistics and the structure of the Milky Way system.

Keeler, James E. American astrophysicist (1857–1900). Director of the Lick Observatory. Noted for his photographic catalogue of nebulae. First to obtain spectroscopic proof (1895) that the rings of Saturn are not solid.

Keill, John. Scottish mathematician and astronomer (1671–1721).

Kepler, Johannes. German mathematician and astronomer (1571–1630). Discovered the three laws of planetary motion and established the idea of the solar system in its modern form.

Kerr, Frank J. Radio astronomer, associated with the Radiophysics Laboratory, Sydney, Australia.

Kohlschütter, A. German astronomer (1882–1942).

Kozyrev, Nikolai A. Soviet astronomer, associated with the Crimean Astrophysical Observatory, U.S.S.R.

Kuiper, Gerard P. American astronomer, Director of the Yerkes and McDonald Observatories.

Laccolith. A dome-shaped mass of igneous rock which, in molten condition, has been forced between strata, causing the overlying rock layers to be domed or arched up.

Lambert, Johann H. German astronomer (1728–1777). Speculated about the parallactic motions of the stars and the structure of the universe.

Lassell, William. English amateur astronomer (1799–1880). Discovered Triton, a satellite of Neptune, and two satellites of Uranus.

Leavitt, Henrietta S. American astronomer (1868–1921). Associated with the Harvard College Observatory, Mass.

Lemaître, Canon Georges. Belgian cosmologist (b. 1894).

Lens. A transparent substance having two optically-worked surfaces, both of which are usually spherical. There are two main types: *Convex*, or thickest in the center and thinnest at the edge, and *Concave*, or thinnest in the center and thickest at the edge.

Leverrier, Urbain J. J. French mathematician (1811–1877). Made important contributions to celestial mechanics.

Libration in latitude. The apparent oscillation of the moon's disk which brings alternately into view small parts of the opposite hemisphere near the north and south limbs.

Libration in longitude. The apparent oscillation of the moon's disk which brings alternately into view small parts of the opposite hemisphere near the east and west limbs.

Liebig, Justus von. German chemist (1803–1873).

Light-year. The distance traveled by light in one year, or approximately six million million miles.

Limb. The edge of the disk of the sun, moon and planets.

Lippershey, Hans. Spectacle-maker of Middelburg, Holland. Constructed in 1608 the first refracting telescope.

Lockyer, Sir J. Norman. English astronomer (1836–1920). Pioneer in spectroscopy, and with Janssen the first to see the solar prominences without total eclipse conditions.

Lowell, Percival. American astronomer (1855–1916). Founder of the Lowell Observatory, Flagstaff, Arizona.

Luminosity. The actual or intrinsic brightness of a star.

Lunar domes. Localized swellings or mounds on the moon's surface similar in appearance to the laccoliths found on the earth.

Lunar month or Lunation. The interval between successive times of new moon. Sometimes called the synodical month.

Lyot, Bernard. French astrophysicist (1897–1952). Inventor of the coronagraph.

Maculae. A term sometimes applied to the dark parts of the moon, or maria, as seen by the unaided eye.

Magellanic clouds. Two patches of misty light visible in southern skies and well removed from the zone of the Milky Way. Both are galaxies, or systems of stars, nebulae and dust, and both appear to be independent from the Milky Way system.

Magnetic field. The region or field around a magnet throughout which the poles of the magnet exert their influence.

Magnitude, Visual. The apparent brightness of a star or other celestial body as compared with some adopted conventional standard. The brightness ratio between successive whole magnitudes is 2·512 to 1, hence a star is 2·512 times as bright as one that is a magnitude fainter.

Maria, Lunar. "Seas", or the great plains on the moon, once thought to be seas.

Marius, Simon. German astronomer (1570–1624).

Mass-luminosity law. The relationship that exists between the mass and the luminosity of a star. Discovered by A. S. Eddington in 1924.

Megacycle. A frequency of vibration of 1 million a second.

Meniscus lens. A "bent" lens, or one with surfaces so arranged that its section is bow- or crescent-shaped.

Meridian. The great circle of the celestial sphere which passes through the celestial poles and the observer's zenith.

Mersenne, Marin. French mathematician (1588–1648).

Messier, Charles. French astronomer (1730–1817). Specialized in hunting comets. Finding that he often mistook nebulae for comets, he put on record (1781) the positions of 103 nebulae.

Meteors. Small bodies circling the sun. They do not become visible until by friction with the earth's upper atmosphere they become incandescent and vaporize. They then appear as "falling stars" or "shooting stars".

Meteorites. Meteors which reach the ground and which can therefore be recovered and studied direct.

Michelson, Albert A. American physicist (1852–1931). Established by experiment the constancy of the velocity of light and thereby helped to pave the way for the Theory of Relativity.

Micrometeorites. Particles of microscopic size which reach the ground from outer space. They are too small to become vaporized during their passage through the atmosphere.

Microscope. An optical instrument for obtaining enlarged views of very small and near objects.

Milky Way, The. A hazy band or zone of light which encircles the heavens. It arises from the combined light of myriads of stars so faint that the unaided eye cannot distinguish the stars individually.

Molecule. The smallest part of a compound that retains chemical identity with the compound.

Monochromatic. Light of a single wavelength, or more generally, light of a single spectral line.

Nasmyth, James. Scottish engineer and astronomer (1809–1890).

Nebula. A term at first applied indiscriminately to all celestial objects of a hazy character which the eye could not resolve into stars. Many of them have since been found to be clusters of stars and galaxies. The term is therefore now applied to wholly gaseous objects, faintly luminous and called also "emission nebulae". Obscuring clouds of interstellar dust are often called "dark nebulae".

Nebulium. The hypothetical substance once thought to be the source of the emission lines in the spectra of gaseous nebulae.

Newton, H. A. American astronomer (1830–1896). Professor of astronomy at Yale College. Specialized in meteor astronomy.

Newton, Sir Isaac. English mathematician and physicist (1642–1727). Founder of celestial mechanics. Introduced the Newtonian telescope and did pioneer experiments in physical optics.

Nicholson, Seth B. Formerly astronomer at the Mount Wilson and Palomar Observatories. An authority on solar phenomena and discoverer of four of Jupiter's satellites.

Nodes. The points in which the orbit of the moon, planet, comet, or artificial earth satellite cuts the plane of the ecliptic.

North celestial pole. The point on the northern part of the celestial sphere towards which the earth's axis of rotation points. Northern stars therefore appear to rotate about this point.

Nova. A temporary or new star in the sense that a faint star already in existence blazes out suddenly, and after remaining visible for a short time, fades into insignificance.

Nova, Recurrent. A nova which brightens more than once.

Nucleus. The central part of an object which, in the case of a comet, is also the brightest.

Object-glass. The main light-collecting and image-forming optical element in a telescope.

Occultation. The disappearance of a celestial body through the interposition of a nearer one, as when the moon hides a star or planet, or a planet hides a star or satellite. A total eclipse of the sun is therefore strictly an occultation of the sun by the moon.

Öhman, Yngve. Swedish astronomer (b. 1903). Professor of Astronomy in the University of Stockholm and Director of the Stockholm Observatory.

Olbers, Heinrich W. M. German astronomer (1758–1840). Discovered Pallas in 1802.

Oort, Jan H. Dutch astronomer (b. 1900). Professor of Astronomy and Director of the Observatory, Leiden. First clearly to demonstrate (1927) the rotation of the Milky Way System.

Open star clusters. Clusters of stars within the Milky Way System.

Opposition. The position of the moon or a planet when it is in a direction diametrically opposite to that of the sun.

Optical doubles. Two stars which as seen from the earth lie in almost the same direction and therefore *appear* to be close together and associated.

Orbit. The imaginary path of a moving celestial body in space.

Orthicon tube. The tube or "heart" of a television camera. It makes possible the scanning of a photoelectric image.

Parabola. A conic section formed by the intersection of a plane with a cone, the plane being parallel to a sloping side of the cone.

Paraboloid. The surface generated by rotating a parabola around its axis.

Parallactic motion of a star. The proper motion of the star due to the sun's motion in space. It varies inversely as the distance of the star from the sun.

Parallax, Trigonometrical. An apparent change in the position of a celestial object due to a real change in the position of the observer.

Parsec. The distance corresponding to a parallax of 1 second of arc. It is equivalent to 3·26 light-years.

Pease, Francis G. American astronomer (1881–1938). Associated with the Mount Wilson Observatory.

Penumbra. The region of semi-shadow over which the illumination gradually increases from total darkness to full illumination.

Perigee. The point on the orbit of the moon or artificial earth satellite which is nearest to the earth.

Perihelion. The point on the orbit of a planet or comet which is nearest to the sun.

Period-luminosity curve. The fairly smooth curve which arises when the periods of cepheid variable stars are plotted against their absolute magnitudes.

Pettit, Edison. Astronomer at the Mount Wilson Observatory.

Photo-electric photometer. An extremely sensitive instrument for measuring the intensity of light. It converts radiant energy into a fast-moving beam of electrons.

Photographic zenith telescope. A photographic telescope mounted so that its optical axis is precisely vertical.

Photometer. An instrument for measuring the intensity of light.

Photometry. The measurement of the intensity of light.

Photon. The smallest quantity of radiant energy in the visual range of the spectrum.

Photosphere. The visible surface of the sun.

Piazzi, Giuseppe. Sicilian astronomer (1746–1826). Director of the Palermo Observatory. Discovered Ceres in 1800.

Pickering, Edward C. American astronomer (1846–1919). Director of the Harvard College Observatory, Cambridge, Mass. Pioneer in stellar photometry and stellar spectrography.

Plages. Extensive luminous clouds of calcium and hydrogen recorded on photographs of the sun taken in the appropriate monochromatic light.

Planetary nebula. Great shells or spheres of glowing gas which have a planetary appearance when seen in the telescope.

Planets. The eight major bodies which, together with the earth, move round the sun and, like the earth, have no light of their own.

Plato. Famous Greek philosopher (about B.C. 428–347).

Polarizing monochromator. A highly-selective optical instrument which permits photographs to be taken in the light of a single color or spectral line.

Population I. Stars, gas and dust found in the neighborhood of the sun and in the outer arms of spiral galaxies.

Population II. Stars of high velocity, the stars found in globular clusters, those found in elliptical galaxies and in the central regions of spiral galaxies.

Porter, John G. American explorer and engineer (1871–1949). Noted for his work in amateur telescope-making and participation in the design of the 200-inch Hale telescope.

Precession of the equinoxes. The slow change in the position of the celestial equator relative to the ecliptic which causes their points of intersection (the equinoctial points) to retrograde along the ecliptic.

Prism. In optical work, a transparent substance bounded by plane-polished surfaces inclined to one another.

Prominences. Immense clouds and sheets of luminous hydrogen gas in the sun's atmosphere.

Proper motion. The angle through which a star appears to move in a year owing to its motion in space relative to the sun.

Proton-proton reaction. A thermonuclear reaction initiated by the collision of two hydrogen nuclei or protons.

Ptolemy, Claudius. Astronomer, who lived at Alexandria in the 2nd century A.D. Wrote on optics and the earth-centered or "Ptolemaic" system of the universe.

Pulsate. To expand and contract in a rhythmical manner.

Pythagoras. Greek philosopher (6th century B.C.).

Radar. A short-wave radio method of determining distance and direction.

Radial velocity. The speed at which a body is approaching or receding from the observer. Sometimes called "line-of-sight velocity".

Radiant. The point or small area in the heavens from which the members of a shower of meteors appear to diverge.

Radiation. The process of the transference of electromagnetic energy from a body across space.

Ray. A single line or narrowest possible beam of light.

Red shift. A displacement towards the red of the Fraunhofer lines in the spectra of distant galaxies. Interpreted as a Doppler-Fizeau effect it means that the galaxies are receding.

Reinmuth, Karl. German astronomer (b. 1892). Formerly director of the Heidelberg Observatory.

Relativity, Theory of. A theory introduced by Albert Einstein founded on the postulate that velocity is relative and extending the Newtonian concepts of space, time and gravitation to concepts of greater generality.

Riccioli, Giovanni Battista. Italian astronomer (1598–1671). Wrote a great treatise on astronomy (1651) in which he introduced the idea of naming the lunar craters and mountains after men of science and philosophers.

Right Ascension (R.A.). The angle which the hour circle drawn through a celestial body makes at either of the celestial poles with the hour circle drawn through the First Point of Aries. It is generally reckoned in hours, minutes and seconds of time.

Ring mountain *see* **Crater (Lunar).**

Ringed plains, Lunar. Large circular areas enclosed by massive mountains. They vary in size from about 50 miles to 180 miles in diameter.

Ritchey, George Willis. American astronomer and optician (1864–1918).

Rosse, Lord. Irish nobleman (1800–1867). Erected in 1845 a 72-inch reflecting telescope at Parsonstown, Ireland. Used the instrument to re-examine many nebulae, and discovered a variety of new features, notably the spiral form of certain nebulae (now known to be spiral galaxies).

Royal Society, The. The major scientific Society in Great Britain, founded in 1660.

Russell, Henry C. American astronomer (1877–1957). Director of Princeton Observatory. Pioneer in the study of the relationship between the spectral classification and absolute magnitudes of the stars.

Sandage, Allan R. Astronomer at the Mount Wilson and Palomar Observatories.

Saros. A period of 223 lunations or 18 years $11\frac{1}{3}$ days after which eclipses tend to repeat themselves in the same order. It approximates closely to the period of revolution of the nodes of the moon's orbit with reference to the sun.

Schiaparelli, Giovanni V. Italian astronomer (1835–1910). Announced in 1877 his discovery of a number of dark lines on the planet Mars which he called "canali".

Schmidt, Bernhard. Estonian astronomer and optician (1879–1935). Invented the Schmidt telescope, a coma-free optical system, in 1929. It consists basically of a concave spherical mirror in front of which is mounted a thin lens or "corrector".

Schwabe, Heinrich. German amateur astronomer (1789–1875). Announced that the number of spots on the sun increased and decreased in a regular way over a period of about 10 years.

Secular acceleration (of the moon's mean motion) A very slow shortening in the moon's period of revolution round the earth. It corresponds to a progressive increase of about 11 secs. a century in the moon's mean motion.

Seismograph. An instrument for recording the frequency and intensity of earth tremors.

Selenography. The study of the physical features of the moon's surface.

Seneca. Famous Stoic philosopher of the 1st century A.D.

Shadow-clock. A primitive form of sundial.

Shapley, Harlow G. American astronomer (b. 1885). Director of the Harvard College Observatory, Cambridge, Mass.

Short, James. London master-optician (1710–1768). Specialized in the manufacture of Gregorian telescopes.

Sidereal month. The period of the moon's revolution round the earth with reference to the stars.

Sidereal year. The time between two successive returns of the sun to the same position among the stars.

Slipher, Vesto M. American astronomer (b. 1875), former director of the Lowell Observatory, Flagstaff, Arizona.

Smart, William M. Regius Professor of Astronomy in the University of Glasgow, Scotland.

Spherical aberration. The inability of a single thin lens or concave spherical mirror to bring parallel rays of light to a single point focus.

Spiral nebula. A galaxy with a spiral or "whirlpool" structure similar to that of M31 in Adromeda or M33 in Triangulum.

Solar apex. The point on the celestial sphere towards which the sun is moving.

Solar year. The time between two successive returns of the sun to the vernal equinox, or First Point of Aries. It is also called the "tropical year".

Spectroheliogram. A photograph of the sun taken with the aid of a spectroheliograph.

Spectroheliograph. An instrument with which the sun can be photographed in monochromatic light.

Spectrohelioscope. An instrument for viewing the solar prominences visually and continuously.

Spectroscope. An instrument for studying spectra.

Spectroscopic binary. A double star with components placed so close together that they cannot be separated optically. Their association is revealed by periodic line-shifts in the absorption lines of their combined spectra.

Spectroscopic parallax. The parallax of a star obtained by studying its spectrum. The spectral characteristics provide pointers to the luminosity of the star. Knowing this and also the apparent brightness of the star, its distance can be found by applying the inverse square law of illumination.

Spectrum, Continuous. The coloured band of light produced when white light (sunlight) is dispersed by an optical prism.

Spencer Jones, Sir Harold. English astronomer (b. 1890). Formerly Astronomer-Royal (1933–1956). Noted for his work in time-determination and for a more accurate determination of the sun's distance based on observations of the asteroid Eros.

Spörer, Gustav. German astronomer (1822–1895).

Stellar interferometer. An instrument which uses the interference of light to measure very small angles between luminous objects, e.g. the diameters of stars.

Struve, Otto. American astronomer, Director of the National Radio Astronomy Observatory, Green Bank, W. Virginia.

Sundial. An instrument for showing the time by means of a shadow cast by the sun on a dial plate.

Sunspots. Dark spots seen at times on the surface of the sun.

Supergiant. A star so great in size that it could contain a large part of the solar system, and so luminous as to equal some 100 to 10,000 suns.

Superior conjunction. The position of a planet when, as seen from the earth, it passes the sun on the far side.

Supernova. An exceptionally bright nova.

Synodic month. The period which elapses between two successive conjunctions of the moon with the sun. Often called a Lunation or Lunar Month.

Synodic period. The period which elapses between two successive conjunctions or oppositions of a planet with the sun.

Tangential velocity. The velocity of a body at right angles to the line of sight.

Telemeter. To transmit instrument recordings from a distance.

Telescope. An optical instrument for obtaining enlarged views of distant objects.

Temporary star *see* **Nova.**

Terminator. The line which divides the dark from the bright or illuminated part of the disk of a planet or of the moon.

Thermal diffusivity. The process of heat distribution and diffusion.

Thermonuclear reaction. The large-scale disintegration of atomic nuclei under conditions of extremely high temperature.

Third quarter. The phase of the moon when it has completed three-quarters of one complete revolution round the earth, relative to the sun. It then appears as a half moon in the morning sky.

Titius, Johann D. German mathematician (1729–1796).

Trapezium. A four-sided figure no two or only two sides of which are parallel.

Twilight. The refracted sunlight, visible after the sun has set or before it rises.

Tycho Brahe. Danish astronomer (1546–1601). Established a magnificent observatory from which he made extensive observations of the positions of the sun, moon and planets.

Ultra-violet. A part of the electromagnetic spectrum just beyond the violet and therefore invisible to the eye.

Umbra. (1) The region of deep shadow or total darkness; (2) The darkest part of a sunspot.

Van Allen radiation belt. A region of high energy electrified particles trapped in the earth's magnetic field.

Wave-front. A surface, every point on which is in the same phase or state of vibration.

Wavelength. The distance that light travels in one complete vibration of the source.

Wave-theory of light. A theory of light clearly enunciated by Thomas Young and Augustin Fresnel early in the 19th century. According to it light is a transverse wave motion in hypothetical medium called the "Luminiferous Ether".

Whipple, Fred L. American astronomer and authority on comets and meteors.

White dwarf. An intensely hot but comparatively small star of high density.

Widmanstätten figure. The pattern of intersecting bands which appears when metallic meteorites are cut, polished and etched with dilute acid.

Wildt, Rupert. German astronomer. Associate professor of astrophysics, Yale University, New Haven, Conn.

Wilson, Alexander. Scottish mathematician (1714–1786). Suggested as a result of observation that many sunspots are saucer-shaped depressions in the photosphere.

With, George H. English amateur astronomer and mirror-maker (1827–1904). Noted for the excellent quality of his astronomical mirrors.

Witt, Karl G. German astronomer (1866–1946). Discovered the asteroid Eros in 1898.

Wolf, Max. German astronomer (1863–1932). Director of the Heidelberg Observatory.

Wolf, Rudolf. Swiss astronomer (1816–1893). Solar physicist and Director of the Berne Observatory. Established the principles of the statistical treatment of sunspot counts.

Wright, Thomas. English mechanic (1711–1786). Suggested in 1750 that the universe is a great disk-shaped system of stars.

X-rays. Radiations of wavelength shorter than those in the ultra-violet. They can readily be produced in the laboratory by bombarding a metal *in vacuo* with a stream of high-velocity electrons.

Zeeman, Pieter. Dutch physicist (1865–1943). In 1896 he observed that spectral lines are split when the source is placed in a strong magnetic field.

Zenith. The point on the celestial sphere vertically overhead.

Zodiac. A band or belt in the sky in which move the sun, moon and planets.

Zodiacal light. A cone-shaped area of light which appears at certain times of the year above the eastern horizon just before dawn, or above the western horizon just after sunset, and remains visible long after twilight has ceased.

Zwicky, Fritz. American astronomer. Professor of astrophysics, California Institute of Technology, Pasadena, Cal.

Index

Page numbers in *italics* refer to captions; items included in the glossary are printed in CAPITALS.